CASES IN
MANAGEMENT STATISTICS

CASES IN MANAGEMENT STATISTICS

With applications from Administration and Finance, Production and Engineering, Sales and Marketing, Research and Development

Norbert Lloyd Enrick
University of Virginia

HOLT, RINEHART AND WINSTON, INC.
New York   Chicago   San Francisco   Toronto   London

CONTRIBUTORS

The invaluable contributions of case materials by the persons listed here are gratefully acknowledged.

G. R. Armstrong
Hunter Spring Division
Ametek, Inc.

Charles A. Bicking
Manager, Mathematics Branch
Research and Development Division
The Carborundum Company

Martin A. Brumbaugh
Bristol Laboratories

Randolph W. Cabell
Systems Engineer
International Business Machines

P. C. Clarke
Vice President, General Manager
Hunter Spring Division
Ametek, Inc.

W. Edwards Deming, Ph.D.
Consultant in Statistical Surveys
Author of *Sample Design in
Business Research* (Wiley, 1960)

Jack H. Dillard
Highway Research Engineer
Virginia Council of Highway
Investigation and Research

Paul E. Green, Ph.D.
Marketing Specialist
E. I. DuPont deNemours Co.

I. Landis Haines
Standards Technical Adviser
Industrial Engineering Division
Lukens Steel Company

W. Capers Harrison
System Meter Supervisor
Virginia Electric and Power Co.

Richard M. Jacobs
Manager
Reliability and Statistical
Research Department
Waltham Laboratories
Sylvania Electric Products Inc.

W. A. Jasson
Supervisor of Reliability
    Laboratory
Airborne Instruments Laboratory
Cutler-Hammer Incorporated

E. H. Lacy
Executive Vice President
Citizens Bank of South Boston

Alvin Lieberman
Manager, Fine Particles Research
Armour Research Foundation
Illinois Institute of Technology

Besse Day Mauss (ret.)
Formerly, Consulting Statistician
Bureau of Ships
United States Navy

Roland H. Noel
Manager, Advertising and Sales
    Promotion
Bristol Laboratories

W. A. Poe
Quality Control Manager
Bennett Pump Division
John Wood Company

F. R. Del Priore
Operational Test and
    Evaluation Forces
United States Navy

Wayne A. Ring
Development Engineer
Barber-Colman Company

W. L. Sandquist
Quality Control Manager
U. S. Instrument Corporation

T. E. Shelburne
Director
Virginia Council of Highway
    Investigation and Research

University of Virginia
Graduate School of Business
    Administration

Charles C. Abbott, Dean
Almarin Phillips, Professor
Christopher T. Collins
Gordon R. Knight
Louis W. Lacy
Jim Moore

Edward C. Varnum
Head, Operations Research
Barber-Colman Company

P. F. Wade
Aluminum Company of Canada,
    Limited
Now with Price, Waterhouse
    and Co.

J. C. Werner
President
Werner Management Consultants

PREFACE

In this age of automation, computers, and management science, business is placing increasing emphasis on executive skills in quantitative analysis. This holds true for producer and consumer industries as well as for service industries, and pervades all major phases of business operation, production, selling, and administration. The graduate who emerges from any school anywhere without at least a one- or two-semester course in statistics would indeed be poorly equipped for a career in business today, and his deficiencies would become all the more marked as the use of quantitative aids in management planning, decision making, and control gains momentum.

Yet, despite these facts, which are only too well known to business and educational leaders, the business school student is apt to have an inadequate appreciation of the future value of his introductory statistics course. Much of the work seems like drudgery to him, because at least in the beginning weeks he will usually fail to see the connection between the statistical techniques he is learning and the important business problems to which these techniques can be applied. So long as the student does not have a full appreciation of how his statistical efforts are likely to be of value in his future career, he will have less interest and expend less effort in statistics than in certain other courses where the connection between learning and future usefulness is practically self-evident, such as management accounting, marketing, and finance.

Recognizing these problems in his own introductory course, the author sought to attain better student motivation by relying on a case-method approach, in which practical problems from actual business situations are used from the outset. The collection presented in this book was thus accumulated. Most of the cases are actual cases. In a few instances the company name is fictitious, and in some cases it was necessary to disguise also product identifications and data. In no instance, however, is the realistic business situation missing. The author hopes that the student will recognize, from the outset, the intimate connection between the statistical techniques advanced and the types of management problems where his learning will be of value.

The book is not designed to replace any existing introductory texts; instead, it aims to supplement these with a collection of cases that fit into the topic areas covered by practically all such texts, for both the one-semester and the two-semester course. In using the cases the author has found the following to be a useful classroom procedure:

1. During the last ten to fifteen minutes of each class meeting, there is a discussion of the case or cases assigned for the next meeting. This discussion includes a brief indication of the significance of the case, the statistical techniques applicable, and a chapter reference to the regular text (and reserve-shelf books) that will be helpful in working out the case.

2. In many instances, such as in various types of control-chart problems, several study groups are formed, and each group is asked to report on one case. Thus two to three reports can be presented in one class meeting, and the various facets of the statistical technique in planning, decision making, and control can be brought out. Many other topics, such as frequency distributions and correlation, lend themselves to similar treatment.

3. After each student presentation, preferably limited to ten minutes, another five minutes can be allowed for classroom discussion. In general, the author has found that in these discussions the students learn more from each other than they could learn from their teacher.

4. When required, depending upon the background of the students and the progress of the class, lectures are interspersed. These may be given either as full class-hour presentations or in conjunction with case assignments. When a good text is used, the amount of lecturing can be minimized. The device of forming

study groups for homework is another means of reducing lectures. In general, the students will benefit far more from what they worked out themselves than from a straight lecture.

In preparing this collection of material, the author realized that the needs, requirements, and preferences of various student groups, teachers, and schools will vary. No doubt there will be selectivity in the use of the material, and there will be most certainly the supplemental use of exercises, problems, and cases from the teacher's own file. Similarly, the order in which the cases are presented in the book need not be the sequence followed in a particular course. Variations are to be expected as normal and desirable, and should not detract from the usefulness of this book.

A broad spectrum of business applications is mirrored in the cases, covering producer and consumer goods and service industries. Not only the productive phases but also the selling, marketing, and administrative applications of statistical techniques are represented. In preparing this material the author has drawn on his consulting experience, and has also relied on material provided by many helpful contributors, as shown on the page following the title page. By obtaining a wide variety of diversified cases, he has hoped that the universal applicability of statistical principles, methods, and techniques in all types of modern business will have been emphasized.

Finally, it should be mentioned that the author has purposely selected case materials that represent data requiring a minimum of calculating drudgery. While a certain amount of pencil pushing and figure work is an essential to learning the statistical principles and techniques pertinent to an introductory course, the point of the introductory statistics course is to present the *essential ideas* of the quantitative approach to planning, decision making, and control. This is accomplished best by going directly to illustrations of useful applications, avoiding such digressions as laborious calculations.

It is the author's hope that these cases will aid the student not only in grasping and retaining *essential ideas*, but in finding the introductory statistics course both interesting and challenging.

Charlottesville, Virginia   NORBERT LLOYD ENRICK
November, 1962

ACKNOWLEDGMENTS

The list of contributors obviously cannot include the names of those individuals and companies who very graciously permitted use of their materials with changed names, places, and related detail.

To many of his students at the Graduate School of Business Administration, and prior thereto at the School of Engineering, of the University of Virginia, as well as to many attendants at industrial training conferences, the author wishes to express his sincere thanks for helpful ideas and suggestions and for constructive criticism, all of which were of value in developing the case method approach contained in this book. To Christopher T. Collins, graduate student assistant, for his meticulous work in assisting in the preparation of materials for this book, a special debt is due.

Finally, the author would like to thank Dean Charles C. Abbott and the Sponsors of the Graduate School of Business Administration at Virginia for allowing the time and resources needed, while at the same time providing much appreciated encouragement, to prepare the case materials herein.

N. L. E.

CONTENTS

CHAPTER V: **REGRESSION AND CORRELATION**

  * Names changed

Introduction

W. EDWARDS DEMING[1]

MANAGEMENT'S USES OF STATISTICAL METHODS

The proper use of statistical techniques in business results in greater output, better quality, uniformity, and reliability of product, and greater returns from sales efforts. Amazingly, these achievements are usually accompanied by reduced cost of production and distribution and without expansion of equipment. Statistical techniques are therefore an important tool of production and distribution. In order to apply these techniques most effectively, top management should not only become familiar with the results of statistical methods but should also study the principles of organization by which to achieve a wider and more effective use of these methods.

Statistical knowledge can contribute vitally toward the maintenance of private enterprise, which, in order to meet the changing demands of the consumer, must depend more and more on increasing the efficiency of the production and distribution systems and on improving the design of product.

[1] Dr. Deming is a noted teacher, research worker, and consultant in statistical surveys. His organizational recommendations near the end of this Introduction should be of special interest.

1

It has been only two decades since statistical control methods came into wide use in the United States and Canada. Other countries have made even more recent starts. The first step to progress in this area was the development of some necessary theory by Shewhart and by Dodge in the early 1930s. A decade later, however, little had actually been done in applying this theory. It was difficult to find examples of control charts being used in American industry, although they were applied in isolated spots. Statistically designed acceptance sampling had gained a somewhat better foothold. Today the situation is entirely different; statistical methods are used widely, and it is difficult to believe that the techniques of statistical control charts, acceptance sampling, survey sampling, and industrial experimentation, which we see in every kind of industry in America, fanned into flame only a few years ago.

But the statistical method is more than just a body of techniques; and it is not merely a collection of figures. It is a mode of thought—it provides management with more reliable answers and results in sharper decisions—especially where competition is keen, where specifications and uniformity are difficult to meet, and where the differences among the performances of materials, machines, and processes are small, but where a wrong decision may cause heavy losses.

STATISTICAL TECHNIQUES AND PRODUCTION

Let us take a look at any production line. It begins with the procurement of raw materials. Material must be received, tested, accepted, rejected, paid for, and sorted for use. The sampling and the tests of materials must make statistical sense, otherwise the buyer or the seller may be subjecting himself to systematic over- or underpayment. Much of the best work in statistical control of quality has been to study the sources of raw materials, in recognition of the fact that a certain amount of uniformity and dependability of raw materials is necessary if a manufacturer wishes to put out good quality himself. But he must define "good" and "uniform" statistically, in terms of the demands of the consumer.

After going through the production line, with its various operations and assemblies, tests, and final inspections, the product starts for the market through various channels of distribution. Sometimes the consumer will be only another department of the same company (often the toughest of all customer to get along with); sometimes he will be another manufacturer; sometimes the consumer will be the great mass of people or families of this nation and of other nations.

Statistical techniques are needed along the whole line of production, which stretches from raw material to consumer, as illustrated conceptually in Figure 1.[2] Astute manufacturers recognize that gaps in statistical work, anywhere along the line, mean losses in production and sales, losses in materials, comparative depreciation in quality, reliability, and uniformity, excessive costs, and ultimate shrinkage of the firm's market.

HOW STATISTICAL TECHNIQUES HAVE AIDED BUSINESS

The impact of statistical theory during the past two decades has been so drastic that it has affected and altered practically every aspect of business, government, and research. Whenever statistical techniques have been applied with competence and conviction, the results have invariably been increased sales and production. The following is a brief outline of some aspects of business that have been hit by this statistical impact.

Production

1. Increased output. Increases of from 10 to 23 percent in output have been reported in the literature. It is important to bear in mind that these increases take place not with increased machinery or floor space, but through more efficient use of men, materials, and machines; improved quality; and less scrap and rework.

A pharmaceutical company reported being able to make a particular antibiotic with only 30 percent as much raw material as it had required six months earlier, before statistical control-chart techniques were introduced. A large steel company reported the saving of one-third of fuel consumption over performance the year before. Such results are not unusual, they are merely illustrative.

2. Better quality and reliability of product at less cost.

3. Greater uniformity at less cost.

4. Improved competitive position through increased production; better quality, uniformity, and reliability; enhanced design; and reduced costs.

5. A meaningful international language by which to (a) express

[2] The application of the statistical quality control from raw materials through receipt of materials, production, consumer research, design, and redesign of product (called by some writers "total quality control"), has been emphasized by Dr. Deming since 1953 and is restated in his address delivered upon receipt of the Shewhart Medal at the 10th annual meeting of the American Society for Quality Control (see *Ind. Qual. Control*, Vol. 8, No. 1, July, 1956).

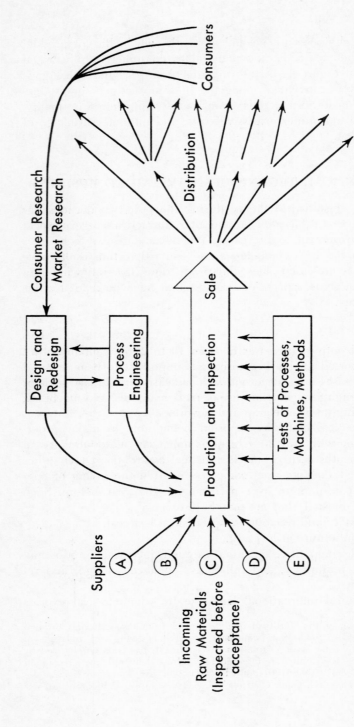

Fig. 1. The industrial production line, from raw material to market, as shown conceptually in this diagram, demands statistical analysis and control at every point in the process. Consumer research should feed back to the design of the product in a continual stream, with design and redesign of product to meet changing demands and requirements as regards quality, cost, and uniformity.

4

standards and specifications of the quality desired and (b) to describe the quality of a product already made.

Management

1. Meaningful performance standards (impossible without statistical techniques) for production, sales, and costs.

2. Meaningful measure of the performance actually attained (impossible without statistical techniques).

3. Improved knowledge of the capabilities of men, materials, machines, and manufacturing processes. (A mistake in accepting a huge contract that calls for greater speed or higher quality than a factory can produce economically may spell ruin. Statistical techniques provide the kind of information and the calculations that management must have for making rational decisions.)

4. Sampling and testing of materials. Statistical techniques provide better knowledge of the weight, quality, and uniformity of a lot or of a series of lots of materials and of their chemical and physical characteristics.

5. Testing and comparison of processes. Processes can be compared for production rate, cost, uniformity, and quality. Statistical techniques provide economical tests and reliable inferences that help management select the most efficient method available.

6. Measurement of costs. Statistical observations give the only reliable information on costs and performance rates, thus providing simultaneously an effective tool by which to increase the efficiency of an operation in production and distribution.

7. Timely approximations on production, sales, shipments, sizes, and activity of accounts for management purposes.

8. The most economical inventories for retail and wholesale stocks and for service.

Marketing and Consumer Research

1. Sampling surveys of consumer preferences.
2. Sales forecasting, long term and short term.
3. Analysis of sales operations, by location, personnel, and products.
4. New product evaluation (in design and development).

Auditing and Accounting

1. Verification and reconciliation of inventories and of accounting records, with improved reliability at less cost.
2. Auditing, with improved reliability at less cost.

3. Current determination of unearned income in intra and inter-company accounting.

Determination of Physical Conditions of Plant; Estimates of Repairs Needed

City Planning

1. Locations of thoroughfares, fire departments, and schools.
2. Treatment of blighted areas.

Safety

More effective administration of a safety program, made possible by statistical definition of significantly high and significantly low rates.

Insurance Rates and Service

Better service through statistical estimates of risks and of frequencies.

Control of Clerical Operations

Better and more accurate results at reduced cost.

Psychometrics

Statistical evaluation of employee tests, training methods, advancement criteria, and general personnel procedures.

Statistical Quality Control

One of the earliest and possibly widest applications of industrial statistics was in the control of quality of production. Statistical quality control is the application of statistical principles and techniques in all stages of production, directed toward the most economic manufacture of a product that is maximally useful and has a market.

Quality is meaningless except in terms of the consumer's demands. Hence the first step in the statistical control of quality is to study the demands of the market. Otherwise a manufacturer may find himself using excellent statistical techniques in production, only to make a beautiful product, economically, for a market that he misjudged.

Statistical methods not only help to produce uniform and dependable quality but they also provide an international language in which to express quality and in which to conduct negotiations, even though buyer and seller are in different parts of the world.

Standardization and Specification

In large part a statistical problem, a standard and a specification serve many requirements. Needs can be determined only by reliable sampling surveys and by reliable tests of performance. Moreover, neither a standard nor a specification has meaning unless it is written in terms of a test that can be brought into statistical control. For example, in the pharmaceutical industry, statistical control of the potency of drugs and vitamins is necessary. Tests of potency must be in control if the dosage is to have meaning.

Statistical System (for Industry and Government)

Through new theory and methods of sampling, coupled with better appreciation for the value of statistics by the business executive, there is now much greater use and less misuse of statistics, with a larger volume and variety of statistics to satisfy the demand through monthly or quarterly surveys. Several federal statistical agencies have not only contributed new theory and methods during the past 20 years, but have also introduced effective organization by which to put these methods into service. The result is reliability tailored to the need; speed; more information per unit cost; controllable precision; and information of known precision.

Financial Planning

1. Forecast of cash inflow, markets, and economic conditions.
2. Budgeting and budgetary control.

CONSUMER RESEARCH

When based on effective statistical surveys, consumer research acts as a governor, or servo-mechanism. A study of the reasons for the likes and dislikes of both consumers and nonconsumers yields predictions that assist management to make informed decisions with respect to changes that should be made now in design, quality, and production levels in order to meet most economically the demand for the product six months or a year from now.

Consumer research is not merely selling, yet it is essential to selling. When it is properly geared to design and production, it is an indispensable modern tool for the problems of the industrial age. Competent consumer research, combined with other statistical techniques, can help to build a firm foundation for private enterprise.

Consumer research is communication between the manufacturer and the users and potential users of his product. When the number of users and potential users is measured in the thousands or millions, this communication can be carried out reliably and economically only by modern statistical procedures. Methods of conducting surveys have changed radically during the past three years, owing to continual improvement of statistical procedures, particularly in sampling, product-testing, experiments for quality, reliability and performance, and in statistical definitions of the information required. Costs of consumer research have decreased in relation to the reliability and usefulness of the results.

Manufacturing and Consumer Research

Manufacturers used to think of manufacturing in three separate and independent steps: (1) design the product, (2) make it, and (3) try to sell it. Success depended on guess-work—guessing what type and design of product would sell and how much of it to make.

Today, modern management introduces, through consumer research, a fourth step, and runs through the four steps in a cycle, over and over.

1. Design the product (with appropriate tests).
2. Make it; test it in the production line and in the laboratory.
3. Put it on the market.
4. Test it in service; through market research, find out what the user thinks of it and why the nonuser has not bought it.
5. (1.) Redesign the product, in the light of consumer reactions to quality and price.

This fourth step was impossible until recently. It could not be carried out economically or reliably without statistical sampling surveys. Intelligent manufacturers always have been interested in discovering the needs and the reactions of the user and of the potential user, but until recently they have had no economical and reliable way of investigating them. The fourth step is communication between the manufacturer and the user and the potential user, thus giving the user a better product, better suited to his needs, and often cheaper. All aspects of consumer research, including evaluation of promotion methods and market potential, forecasting of trends and developments, analysis of sales operation, and considerations of distribution channels and procedures rely heavily on sound application of statistical principles and techniques.

ORGANIZING TO EXPAND USE OF STATISTICAL TECHNIQUES

No particular organization chart will fit exactly everywhere, but it is possible to lay down some general principles.

1. Statistical techniques should be used wherever they may be found useful and not just in the area where they happen to grow up. A company cannot afford to do excellent work with control charts in

one part of the plant while it permits the sampling and testing of incoming materials or its consumer research to sag into lower grade.

2. Statistical techniques should not be administratively subordinate to production, inspection, consumer research, or design, yet they must serve all these functions. Statistical work cannot be directed by someone who has no knowledge of statistical principles any more than research in thermodynamics could be directed by an accountant. It has been advocated that the statistical administrator should enjoy a position similar to that of the comptroller, whose job is to report his findings for the good of the company.

3. The organization must be one in which new ideas have a chance to be heard and to be implemented. The nonstatistician is not the one to evaluate, to encourage, or to discourage a new statistical idea, however helpful he may be.

4. The use of statistical methods is not mere "application." There can in fact be no application without theory to apply, just as there can be no knowledge without research. The most valuable statistician is the one who knows the most theory and who is capable of adapting it and explaining what he wishes to do with it. Statistical techniques are not "installed"; they must be rooted and nourished with patience, support, and recognition from top management. They do not blossom out suddenly. They may even lead to mistakes now and then along the route to better procedures, processes, and products.

5. Statistical knowledge cannot be paid for by dollars alone. Employment of qualified people, library facilities, and opportunity for study and attendance at statistical meetings and courses are important. The placement of statistical techniques in the operations where they will be most productive is primarily a problem in management. Why? Because statistical knowledge is a rare but productive commodity along the entire line of business activity from raw material to the consumer and back again.

The principal role of data collection and its reduction and statistical analysis in a suitable form for managerial decision-making is illustrated in Figure 2, which shows how all major phases of a business operation are vitally dependent on these statistical activities.

A good organization must include in its structure provisions whereby statistical ability can be shifted about and directed toward whatever problems are most pressing from time to time. This organization charges someone with the duty of discovering what problems confronting the company can be solved by means of statistical methods and then finding the best possible solutions.

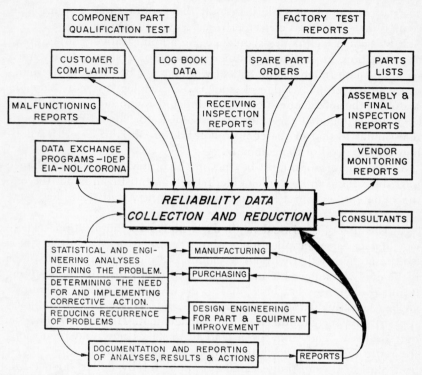

Fig. 2. The principal role of data collection and its subsequent reduction and statistical analysis, providing useful information in a suitable form for managerial decision making. The diagram shows the application of this principle to the maintenance of high reliability (and thus minimal failures) in electronics production, emphasizing how all major phases of operations are dependent on this information. (Illustration courtesy of Sylvania Electronic Systems)

Functions of the Statistical Administrator[3]

A new profession is at hand—the statistical administrator. His title is not important; his function is. Among his qualifications are (1) knowledge of statistical principles and of the power of statistical techniques; (2) ability to recognize statistical problems when he sees them, in any part of the production line, whether they lie in sampling of materials, high costs in certain operations, variable results in sales, evaluation of consumer research, development of new products, standardization, or other areas.

[3] Dr. Deming's views in this and the following sections may be of special interest for discussion.

He need not be a renowned statistician. He will hire people with knowledge of theory and he will be responsible for putting them to work where the problems are most pressing. He will be responsible for the promotions of these people, which will, of course, be based on results. In this way, people that help the company to produce a better product, more economically, by the aid of statistical theory, will be rewarded.

Costs of Inadequate Statistical Organization

Where business fails to provide proper statistical organization, it suffers continued waste of materials, manpower, and machinery; ineffective sampling and testing for the purchase or distribution of materials; wrong statistical information on markets and sales; ineffectual analyses and incorrect applications of current government statistical reports; and lack of operating intelligence through failure to summarize internal reports and accounts.

Professor Holbrook Working of Stanford University observed, in the days when statistical techniques were just beginning to be used in business, that the companies which seemed to make the most rapid strides were the small ones. One explanation is that a new idea has a better chance in a small company and that horizontal motion from one point in the business to another is usually easier in small companies. In too many big companies one finds superb statistical ability, but it is helpless and useless because it is bound by an inflexible vertical organization that has no coordinated direction from the top of the staff.

Industry cannot suddenly create hundreds of statisticians, but it can create the type of organization that will maximize the statistical knowledge that the company possesses.

An Example of Statistical Organization

The organization of the statistical work in the Bureau of the Census is a good example to study. Each division has a statistician, who works on the sampling problems of the division—population, agriculture, manufacturing, business, exports. His collaboration and interest in the problems of the division must be acceptable to the division chief, but for his statistical techniques he is responsible only to the assistant director for statistical standards, which is an over-all staff function of the entire Bureau. The advancement of the statistician in a division depends on the recommendations of the assistant director. Thus the statistician in the Bureau is a servant of the division, his main job being improvement of the statistical work therein.

In this type of organization, statistical ability is not buried in the brush of administrative misunderstanding, but is nourished and thrives. Small wonder that people come from all over the world to study the statistical methods and organization of the Census Bureau.

Growing Need for Statisticians

A number of universities now teach statistical theory. But for every high-grade research man, industry and government need hundreds of men in statistical administration—men who think in terms of statistics, who know statistical theory as power, who see problems first and techniques second, who know statistical methods, and who have the ability to derive new theory for new problems.

Statistical teaching should recognize the vital power in the application of statistical theory and in statistical thinking. Schools of engineering, commerce, and business administration should teach statistical theory, not as an end in itself but from the functional angle, as power in the solution of man's problems.

Chapter *I*

BASIC STATISTICAL ANALYSIS:
FREQUENCY DISTRIBUTIONS,
AVERAGES, AND VARIABILITY

COLGATE JERSEY CITY PLANT

Frequency-distribution Analysis
in Soap-cake Production

Data obtained from testing and inspection are often useful for continuous control of production processes. In addition, valuable information about the variability of the production process can be obtained from a review of accumulated data.

Table I-1 shows the results of tests to determine the amount of volatile matter in soap. Tests were performed on successive production lots, using four sampling specimens (cakes of soap) selected at random from each lot. The sampling results, in terms of the total of the four specimens, the sample average, and the sample range, are also shown.

QUESTIONS

Analyze the test data from a viewpoint of obtaining pertinent information concerning the characteristics of the production process as regards:

13

1. Frequency distribution pattern.

2. Standard deviation and variation coefficient.

3. Process capability analysis, with suggested tolerances based on this capability.

4. Prepare a report summarizing your findings, confining yourself to not more than two typewritten pages (double-spaced) and not more than three exhibits.

TABLE I-1.   AMOUNT VOLATILE MATTER IN SOAP, PERCENT

Lot No.*	Sampling Specimen Number				Sample Results		
	1	2	3	4	Total	Average	Range
1	35.37	35.22	34.64	35.29	140.52	35.13	0.73
2	34.99	34.77	34.97	34 96	139.69	34.92	.22
3	34.29	34.24	34.32	34.27	137.12	34.28	.08
4	34.20	34.75	34.03	34.59	137.57	34.39	.72
5	34.36	34.69	34.23	34.40	137.68	34.42	.46
6	34.50	34.24	34.37	34.25	137.36	34.34	.26
7	34.53	34.47	34.83	34.43	138.26	34.57	.40
8	35.88	34 43	34.79	34.58	139.68	34.92	1.45
9	N.G.	34.78	34.53	35.13	104.44	34.81	.60
10	34.71	34.69	34.95	35.58	139.93	34.98	.89
11	35.31	34.85	34.54	34.32	139.02	34.76	.99
12	34.24	34.20	34.04	34.14	136.62	34.16	.20
13	34.32	35.44	34.35	34.50	138.61	34.65	1.12
14	34.46	34.91	34.32	34.31	138.00	34.50	.60
15	34.30	34.13	34.56	34.51	137.50	34.38	.43
16	34.24	34.41	34.26	34.16	137.07	34.27	.25
17	34.85	34.43	34.72	34.93	138.93	34.73	.50
18	34.53	34.02	34.09	33.50	136.14	34.04	1.03
19	34.41	33.83	34.39	32.86	135.49	33.87	1.55
20	34.08	34.40	34.06	34.68	137.22	34.31	.62
21	33.72	34.39	33.75	33.39	135.25	33.81	1.00
22	32.85	33.76	33.60	33.32	133.53	33.38	.91
23	34.39	34.08	34.66	34.18	137.31	34.33	.58
24	34.20	33.39	33.28	33.99	134.86	33.72	.92
25	32.90	33.33	33.67	33.27	133.18	33.29	.77
26	34.20	34.10	33.91	34.15	136.36	34.09	.29
27	33.31	34.73	34.41	34.70	137.15	34.29	1.42
28	34.97	35.84	35.06	34.95	140.82	35.20	.89
29	34.02	34.02	35.19	34.59	137.82	34.45	1.17
30	34.41	33.88	34.10	34.69	137.08	34.27	.81

* These are successive production lots tested.

CUTLER-HAMMER, INCORPORATED

Electronic-parts Reliability Control through Analysis of Frequency-distribution Patterns

The mounting complexity of control systems and space-age instrumentation forces statistical techniques into the forefront of vital analytical methods. Airborne Instruments Laboratory, a division of Cutler-Hammer, Incorporated, uses statistical techniques as a means of effectively and economically accomplishing the following aims:

1. Evaluating performance, reliability, and accuracy of equipment produced.

2. Determining confidence intervals and significance levels for various component parts and subassemblies.

3. Designing experiments and analyzing results, as a part of continuing research to develop new and improved systems.

As an illustration of the application of these statistical techniques, the data below, obtained by random sampling of 20 10K-ohm carbon composition transistors from a vendor's shipment checked on an ohmmeter, are discussed.

Resistance	No. of Units	Resistance	No. of Units
7.5K	0	10.5	2
8.0	2	11.0	3
8.5	1	11.5	1
9.0	2	12.0	0
9.5	4	12.5	1
10.0	4	13.0	0

In spite of the limited amount of test data on hand, a frequency distribution can be plotted, and the actual frequencies can be compared against those expected from a normal curve. When this is done for the above data, a little-realized hazard in specifying tolerances becomes apparent: If one buys component parts to a loose tolerance, the order probably will be filled from residual units, after all tighter tolerance orders have been filled. One will thus receive units falling into the tail areas of the distribution curve. It is therefore advisable to specify part tolerances only after determining the range of values that can be allowed for the circuits or mechanical assemblies and after providing an appropriate further margin of safety.

As system complexity increases, the difficulty and necessity of measuring system reliability mounts. A system-reliability diagram must be prepared, tracing the interdependencies of components with respect to the ability of one part or circuit to work even though another malfunctions. Next, hazard rates must be evaluated, such as "failures per million hours," representing the expected malfunctions of component parts within each segment of the reliability diagram. The overall systems tolerance can then be determined by combining the individual component evaluations.

By constantly improving the confidence levels associated with hazard rates, the limiting factors in overall reliability of increasingly complex systems are being overcome. Research, aided by such statistical techniques as multiple regression and correlation analysis, multi-factor-variance analysis, and differential-tolerance combination, accompanied by statistical quality-control applications, represents the primary means of achieving increased reliability for space-age instrumentation. In the last analysis, reliability accomplishments represent the success of the combined efforts of management, engineering, statistical, and supervisory personnel within an organization.

BRISTOL LABORATORIES, INCORPORATED (A)[1]

Frequency-distribution Analysis of Production Stream

In order to establish a manufacturing specification for tablet thickness of a particular product, the individual thicknesses of 200 tablets, taken from the production stream, were tabulated as shown in Table I-2.

QUESTIONS

What conclusions would you draw from a frequency distribution plot analysis, assuming the following:

1. The 200 tablets were taken from two machines.
2. The 200 tablets were taken from one machine.

[1] Division of Bristol Myers Company.

TABLE I-2. MEASURED THICKNESS OF 200 TABLETS
FROM PRODUCTION STREAM

Thickness (maximum diameter in inches, measured to nearest thousandth)	Number of Tablets
0.238	2
.239	13
.240	32
.241	29
.242	18
.243	21
.244	20
.245	22
.246	22
.247	13
.248	3
.249	0
.250	1
.251	1
.252	0
.253	1
.254	0
.255	2
Total	200

PEYTON PISTON AND BEARINGS COMPANY

Grinding Operation on Cylindrical Parts, Evaluated through Normal-curve Analysis

The company was considering the production, on a subcontract basis, of a pin required to be ground to a diameter of one inch, with a tolerance of plus and minus 0.0006 inch. From a sampling of the available grinding machine on the production floor, it was determined that the machine could produce these parts to a standard deviation of 0.0003 inch, with a normal distribution.

It seemed obvious that the firm could not meet the tolerances with the available equipment. The plant manager, however, was anxious to get the order. In particular, he pointed out that, so long as no under-sized parts were produced (which would be "scrap"), any oversized parts could always be "ground down" to the required dimension. The production engineer agreed.

In setting up the grinding machine, towards what average dimension should it be aimed to produce practically no scrap while at the same time keeping the pins to be reground to a minimum?

QUESTIONS

1. The recommended average dimension towards which the grinding operation should be aimed, in inches.

2. The percent of pins to be reground under the setting recommended.

UNITED STATES INSTRUMENT CORPORATION

Statistical Analysis of Vendor Quality, Using Frequency Plot

As part of an intensive reliability control program, United States Instrument Corporation maintains a thoroughly worked out program of receiving inspection for purchased parts. A check of a shipment of 2,000 bushings, Part No. 1382-1, supplied by one vendor, yielded the following results:

Sample No.	Dimension (In.) for Each of Five Bushings Tested					Sample Range
1	0.169	0.158	0.162	0.167	0.161	0.011
2	0.165	0.163	0.164	0.162	0.165	0.003
3	0.165	0.164	0 165	0.165	0.165	0.001
4	0.164	0.164	0.159	0.165	0.163	0.006
5	0.165	0.163	0.164	0.164	0.162	0.003
6	0.165	0.164	0.166	0.164	0.158	0.008
7	0.159	0.162	0.161	0.165	0.165	0.006
8	0.162	0.164	0.163	0.165	0.164	0.003
9	0.167	0.164	0.164	0.164	0.164	0.003
10	0.166	0.165	0.167	0.165	0.168	0.003
					Total	0.047

In evaluating these findings against the specified dimension of 0.164± 0.004 in., the following was determined:

1. Percent of bushings in the total sample that (a) failed to meet the upper specification tolerance, and (b) fell below the lower specification tolerance.

2. The percentages of nonconforming parts that would have been expected from a normal curve distribution.

3. A plot of the actual distribution of the sample of 50 bushings.

The sharp disagreement of the results from 1 and 2 was noted, and the desirability of further analyses received consideration.

HUNTER SPRING COMPANY

Frequency Patterns in Vendor-vendee Relations

For many years now Hunter Spring Company, of Lansdale, Pennsylvania, submits with each shipment a quality report, containing the results of testing of 50 randomly sampled parts in the lot. The results are reported in the form of a frequency distribution, and have found considerable popularity among its customers.

In stressing the value of frequency patterns, Hunter Spring Company has prepared diagrams (Figs. I-1 and I-2) of typical patterns that may be observed by a vendor checking his own product or a vendee checking a shipment received.

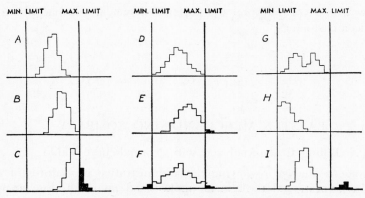

Fig. I-1. Frequency-distribution patterns

QUALITY REPORT No. 4823

PRODUCT _COMPRESSION SPRING_ CUSTOMER ___ QUOT. No. _87884-8_
CHARACTERISTIC _P @ L OF 0.180"_ PART NO. _9008243_ REF. ___
INSP. METHOD _217-PM_ SPECIFIED LIMITS _200 GRAMS ± 5% @ 0.180"_
SAMPLE DRAWN _AFTER CAD. PLATE_ EQUIV. INSP. LIMITS _190 – 210 GRAMS @ 0.180"_

HPS ORDER No.		80710 (15M)	82444 (5M)	
CUSTOMER ORDER No.		116649	117243	
INSPECTED BY		RHD E.D.C.	V.g.S.	
DATE		1-6-48 1/7/48	2-9-48	
FORCE (P)		LOT 1	LOT 2	
	MIN.			
190				
2		//	//	//
4		ᚋᚋ ////	ᚋᚋ //	ᚋᚋ ///
6		ᚋᚋ ᚋᚋ ᚋᚋ //	ᚋᚋ ᚋᚋ ////	ᚋᚋ ᚋᚋ ᚋᚋ ///
8		ᚋᚋ ᚋᚋ ᚋᚋ /	ᚋᚋ ᚋᚋ ᚋᚋ ///	ᚋᚋ ᚋᚋ ᚋᚋ ᚋᚋ ///
200		ᚋᚋ ᚋᚋ /	ᚋᚋ ////	ᚋᚋ ᚋᚋ ᚋᚋ ᚋᚋ ᚋᚋ
2		///	ᚋᚋ	ᚋᚋ ᚋᚋ ᚋᚋ //
4			/	ᚋᚋ ᚋᚋ
6				ᚋᚋ /
8				//
210	MAX.			/
		OK	OK	OK
		8100 PCS.	7M PCS	5100 PCS
		C.J.M.	C.J.M.	C.J.M.

Fig. I-2. Typical frequency plot provided by the vendor. (Courtesy Hunter Spring Company)

QUESTIONS

How would you interpret the patterns shown, if you had obtained them as a customer?

RALSTEN MERCHANDISING COMPANY

Billing Costs Analyzed with Normal-curve Table

A systems analyst, reviewing the administrative procedures of the company, questioned the use of jumbo-sized invoice forms, since a box of 100 continuous forms with 5 carbon interleafings cost $4, while on the other hand regular forms cost only $3 per box of 100. Moreover, while the jumbo form provided space for 20 separate items per invoice, it was found from a sampling check that the average invoice needed only 11 separate items to be listed, which is below the 12 items accommodated by the regular form.

It would have been impractical to have two sets of billing forms. The systems analyst, therefore, recommended that the regular forms be used throughout, and that in those instances where a regular form did not provide enough space for all charges, two invoices be made out to that account.

The office manager preferred to stick with the jumbo-sized form. He emphasized that there were about a thousand billings per day, that certainly a portion of them would now require two regular invoices where previously only one jumbo-sized invoice was required, and that the additional clerical and procedural complexities introduced by each such occurrence would involve approximately two cents extra cost.

QUESTIONS

Assuming the data as given to be correct, with whom do you agree and why?

UNIWEB DISTRIBUTORS, INCORPORATED

Market Analysis Using Weighted Averages and Indexes

Uniweb Distributors is the selling house for Unispin Yarn Mills and Uniweb Weavers. Uniweb Distributors had developed a special market analysis program, designed to evaluate the expected customer demand for a wide range of fabric styles and patterns at the outset of each year's selling season. Demand during the peak season months exceeded normal mill capacity, so that it was impossible to produce only after orders had been received. Consequently, manufacturing commitments in terms of raw stock purchases, spinning and dyeing of yarn, weaving, and finished-goods-inventory buildup, had to be made early in the season.

Program

The market-analysis program was aimed at distinguishing early in the season between patterns that would be likely to "catch on" and others that might not find favor and, if produced for stock, would thus end up as "distress goods" sold at a loss. Two major program phases were developed:

1. Preseason surveys of pattern preferences, based on an evaluation of preference ratings by various individuals.
2. Early season purchases of sample yardages by customers, indicative of the actual trends developing, and expressed in terms of *trend ratings*.

The preference rating points from phase 1 were then combined with the trend rating points from phase 2 to obtain an over-all rating for each pattern.

Using swatches of the various experimental patterns developed before the start of the season, various persons were interviewed and asked to indicate their preferences. The standard question asked was, "How do you like this design for ——— goods," with the blank line filled in with "dress goods," "men's sportswear," or other item, as might be appropriate. Employees, customers' buyers, and store personnel dealing directly with the buying public were included in the survey. Each person's response was based on a preference rating list, which in turn was keyed to rating points, as illustrated below:

Preference Designation	Preference Rating Points
Superior	100
Very Good	90
Good	80
Fair	70
Adequate	60
Just Passable	50
Questionable	40
Inferior	30
Unacceptable	20

Table I-4 shows how the preference points were evaluated for a particular style, thus providing a preliminary indication of the degree of popularity to be expected.

Early Season Sample Sales

Very early in the season, the trend of sales of sample yardages to customers serves as an indication of the market that may be developing for each pattern. A typical evaluation is illustrated in Table I-5. For each pattern, the sample yardages purchased by a customer are shown in parentheses. After the customer has had a chance to cut and sew his own styles and show them to his trade, he may be expected to order regular yardage quantities. An indicator of the yardage he may thus order is given by the customer's sales ratio. Assume, for example, that customer Jones has in the past purchased 400 yards for every one yard sampled. Then his sales ratio, in terms of 100's of yards, would be $400/(1 \times 100)$, which works out to a ratio of 4. Next, by multiplying the sample yardages by the sales ratio, the expected yardage sales are developed.

TABLE I-4. PRESEASON PREFERENCE SURVEY. EXAMPLE OF PREFERENCE RATING POINTS FOR ONE STYLE

Grader	Patterns in Style					
	A	B	C	D	E	F
Poole	70	50	70	50	40	80
Parks	90	50	80	50	50	80
Prinz	80	60	80	30	40	70
Pratt	70	50	70	70	30	90
Plain	60	60	90	60	20	80
Pruit	70	70	90	40	60	80
Pangs	60	30	80	50	30	70
Pruen	70	50	80	50	50	90
Average of Preference Rating Points	71	53	80	50	40	80

Observation: Patterns C and F have received an average of 80 points each, representing a preference rating of "good." Pattern A with 71 points represents "fair" rating. All other patterns, having received relatively low points, are not likely to be successful sellers.

Each individual yardage sales estimate is highly tentative and may be considerably off on either the high or low side. However, when totaling the individual estimates of all customers on a particular pattern, some of the excessively high figures will usually be balanced by unduly low figures. As a result the over-all pattern estimate should be a useful indicator of the market trends developing for each such pattern.

In the example in Table I-5, pattern C has the highest expected yardage of 75,000 and therefore receives the highest rating of 100 trend points. The next highest pattern, F, receives 15 points less, or 85 trend points. Proceeding similarly for all patterns, trend points are assigned. The interval of 15 points was chosen to provide a suitable

TABLE I-5. EARLY SEASON SAMPLING. TREND RATING BASED ON PURCHASES
OF SAMPLING YARDAGES BY CUSTOMERS

Customer	Sales Ratio*	Patterns**					
		A	B	C	D	E	F
Jones	4.0	(8)		(10)			(6)
		32		40			24
Allen	20.0	(9)		(20)			(10)
		180		400			200
Green	2.0		(4)		(2)	(4)	
			8		4	8	
Smith	10.0	(7)	(5)	(8)	(5)	(4)	(8)
		70	50	80	50	40	80
Worth	8.0	(6)		(5)			(5)
		48		40			40
Cairn	6.0			(10)	(4)		(5)
				60	24		30
Coles	12.0	(4)	(4)	(8)			(8)
		48	48	96			96
Davis	4	(4)	(5)	(10)	(4)	(4)	(5)
		16	20	40	16	16	20
Sales Expected, in 100's of Yards		394	126	750	94	64	490
Trend Points		70	55	100	40	25	85

* From past experience, ratio = yards sold (in 100's)/yards sampled.
** Under each pattern, parentheses show sample yards purchased. Regular figures show expected yards to be sold in 100's obtained by multiplying sales ratio × sample yards.

range of points for all patterns. If there had been more patterns, such as 12 in place of the present 6, only 7 or 8 points in place of 15 points would have been used for the decrease in points from one pattern to the next.

Over-all Pattern Rating

In order to obtain an over-all rating for each pattern, the preference points and trend points were combined, after weighting them by 40 and 60 percent each. The resultant over-all rating points thus obtained for each pattern served management in the coordination of production with sales and in planning inventories in anticipation of peak-season requirements. Large stocks of unpopular patterns and shortages of patterns in high peak-season demand were thus minimized.

QUESTIONS

Prepare a table showing the over-all rating points for each of the patterns in Tables I-4 and I-5.

GORDON PRESSED STEEL COMPANY

Averaging Production Rates

The primary business of Gordon Pressed Steel Company was the production of metal parts for subassemblies. In determining the cost for a new job, on which bids were to be placed, the time study engineer had prepared the following estimates for the various operations:

Operation Performed	Production Rate (Parts per Hour)
Blank	50
Drop-hammer	100
Punch	25
De-bur	20

Operator pay for each of these operations is about the same, approximately $2 per hour. Each part, before it is completed, must undergo the 4 processing operations in the sequence shown above.

QUESTIONS

Determine (1) the average production rate in parts per hour; (2) the approximate labor cost in dollars per part.

UNIBLEND LABORATORIES, INC.

Fineness Determinations Using Weight-length Data

John McKenna, a fiber technologist in the employ of Uniblend Laboratories, was engaged in contract research on fiber blending for a large chemical company. He was particularly concerned with the

effects of various fiber fineness properties on fiber blends. Fiber fineness is measured in terms of weight per linear length of fiber, the
customary expression being "micrograms per inch."

Blending of Batches

John blended (or mixed) together two batches of fiber staple, each
weighing one pound. Batch A consisted of fibers with a fineness of 2
micrograms per inch, while batch B had a fineness of 3 micrograms
per inch. The fibers in batch B were thus not as fine (or "coarser") as
the fibers in batch A.

Blending of Filaments

Next, John twisted together two 1000-yard lengths of filament on
the laboratory twisting machine.

Filament A had a fineness of 2 micrograms per inch, while filament
B had a fineness of 3 micrograms per inch.

QUESTIONS

What is the average fineness of the thoroughly blended new batch?
What is the average fineness of the twisted strand produced?

STANDARD CABLE COMPANY

Frequency-distribution Analysis of Tensile Strengths

Tensile strengths of cable Type X-106, produced by Standard Cable
Company, are shown in Table I-6.

QUESTIONS

Using the data, determine the following:

1. Arithmetic mean, median, and mode.
2. Standard deviation, using unbiased sums-of-squares method.
3. Coefficient of variation.
4. Average range.
5. Standard deviation estimated from average range.
6.* Control chart limits for sample averages, based on 3-sigma
limits.

* These assignments involve methods usually brought out in a later part of a
statistics course and will usually be assigned at a later time as a supplemental
analysis of the frequency distribution.

7.* Control chart limits for sample averages, based on 2-sigma limits.

8.* Control limits for ranges (3-sigma).

9.* Variance analysis, sums-of-squares method, of between-lot variation, as against within-lot variation.

10.* Is the between-lot variation significant?

11. Plot a frequency-distribution pattern.

TABLE I-6. STRENGTHS OF SAMPLES OF CABLE

Tensile Strengths in 100's of Pounds, Obtained on an Instron Tester

Lot No. 1	Lot No. 2	Lot No. 3	Lot No. 4	Lot No. 5	Lot No. 6	Lot No. 7
44	45	45	46	48	47	47
49	47	46	47	46	47	47
45	44	45	47	46	47	45
47	46	46	42	45	44	43
46	47	47	47	46	46	46
46	46	46	43	48	46	47

Lot No. 8	Lot No. 9	Lot No. 10	Lot No. 11	Lot No. 12	Lot No. 13	Lot No. 14
44	47	48	45	45	47	45
46	46	46	46	46	45	46
46	50	43	48	49	46	47
47	46	43	46	46	47	45
46	45	45	45	48	46	46
48	45	45	47	48	46	46

Lot No. 15	Lot No. 16	Lot No. 17	Lot No. 18	Lot No. 19	Lot No. 20	Lot No. 21
46	45	48	44	45	45	49
49	45	45	47	44	46	45
47	46	47	46	45	46	47
46	47	46	47	44	45	46
47	46	45	45	47	44	47
46	45	45	46	46	47	45

* These assignments involve methods usually brought out in a later part of a statistics course and will usually be assigned at a later time as a supplemental analysis of the frequency distribution.

Chapter II

CONTROL CHARTS IN PRODUCTION, MANAGEMENT, AND ADMINISTRATION

MONSANTO CHEMICAL COMPANY, PLASTICS DIVISION

Statistical Analysis of Molded Bases, Using Control Charts for Averages and Ranges

In the molding operation of a plastic base for an electrical component, the most important characteristic was considered to be the length of the base, since this was required to fit snugly into the final assembly.

A sampling of the production process yielded the best results shown in Table II-1, showing the length dimension in terms of a ten-thousandth of an inch plus the basic dimension of 1.6000 inches.

QUESTIONS

Prepare a brief report based on your analysis of the following questions:

1. Is the production process under good control, as regards fluctuations in average level and variability?

28

2. What tolerances for base length is the present production process capable of holding?

Confine your report to not more than 2 double-spaced pages of text and 2 pages of exhibits.

TABLE II-1.   PLASTIC BASE LENGTHS

Measurements in Ten-Thousandths of an Inch Plus the
Basic Dimension of 1.6000 In.**

Sample Number	May					
	1	2	3	4	5	6
1	504*	503	481	482	489*	469
2	458*	496	471	499*	479	489
3	479	481*	455*	462*	478	462*
4	478	504*	487*	475	468	495*
5	477	482	487	481	467*	484
Total	2396	2466	2381	2399	2381	2399
Average	479	493	476	480	476	480
Range	46	23	32	37	22	33

Sample Number	May					
	8	9	10	11	12	13
1	489	477	466	493	484	478
2	487	478*	480	464*	461*	476*
3	466	478	496*	479	481	477
4	507	478	459*	510*	480	494*
5	506	460*	481	475	514	476
Total	2455	2371	2382	2421	2420	2401
Average	491	474	476	484	484	480
Range	41	18	37	46	53	18

Sample Number	May					
	15	16	17	18	19	20
1	468	479*	490	478	469	451*
2	449*	491	484	485	476	467
3	470	475	487	477*	457*	495
4	489	480	468*	480	466	484
5	493*	502*	497*	496*	477*	513*
Total	2369	2418	2426	2416	2345	2410
Average	474	484	485	483	469	482
Range	54	32	29	19	20	62

* High or low test result.
** For example, the entry value 504 = 1.6504 in.

MONROE CALCULATING MACHINE COMPANY

Control Charts for Pin-grinding Operation

The data shown in Table II-2 represent inspection results of a pin-grinding operation. Measurements are made on a dial gauge by a competent inspector, using carefully calibrated inspection and testing equipment.

QUESTIONS

Complete Table II-2 by entering the sample averages, ranges, and "unbiased" estimates of the standard deviations in the spaces provided for this purpose. Next, on the basis of the data available, answer the following questions:

1. Is the production process meeting the specification for outside pin diameter of 0.1600 in. plus and minus 0.0015 in.?

TABLE II-2. INSPECTION RESULTS FROM SAMPLING OF PINS,
OUTSIDE DIAMETER AFTER GRINDING

	June 1	June 2	June 3	June 5	June 6
	0.1601	0.1598	0.1597	0.1598	0.1599
	.1599	.1601	.1602	.1602	.1601
	.1600	.1603	.1603	.1604	.1602
	.1603	.1602	.1602	.1601	.1604
	.1602	.1599	.1601	.1600	.1600
Average					
Range					
Std. Dev.					

	June 8	June 9	June 10	June 11	June 12
	0.1602	0.1603	0.1602	0.1601	0.1601
	.1604	.1605	.1603	.1597	.1602
	.1600	.1597	.1604	.1598	.1599
	.1597	.1602	.1605	.1605	.1598
	.1600	.1603	.1600	.1604	.1600
Average					
Range					
Std. Dev.					

1. Specified dimension is 0.1600 ± 0.0015 inch.
2. Each entry is the result of one dial gage reading on a randomly selected pin.
3. Part No. B-298, dept. L-1, machine L-8, operation L-4, operator C. P., inspector E.W.S.

2. How would you propose that production be controlled on a current or daily basis in the future?

ALUMINUM COMPANY OF CANADA, LIMITED

Analysis of Cast-to-Cast Variation,
Using Average and Range Charts

Production of extruded lengths of an alloy involved the following operations: (1) melting and blending in a remelt furnace of the proper alloy constituents, (2) pouring and casting the molten metal to form, (3) sawing apart each cast length into several ingots of specified length, and (4) extrusion of each sawed ingot to produce the extruded lengths (Fig. II-1). These lengths were kept in production lots identified by the cast number from which they had been extruded.

Of the various tests performed on each cast, one of the most important was the determination of tensile strength, usually made on

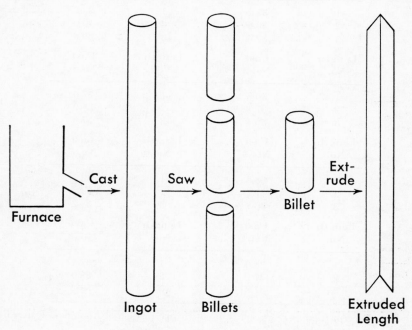

Fig. II-1. Production process (schematic)

three randomly chosen extruded lengths. Typical test results are shown in Table II-3.

The superintendent of quality control decided that two types of statistical analyses would be desirable:

1. Control charts for sample averages and ranges, based on 3-sigma limits, for use by personnel concerned with routine production.

2. An analysis of variance of within- and between-cast variations, for use by the development engineer in charge of process improvement.

QUESTIONS

Prepare the first analysis. Later, when you are familiar with variance-analysis techniques, you may be asked to prepare the second.

TABLE II-3. STRENGTH OF EXTRUDED LENGTHS OF ALLOY A

Tensile in Pounds per Square Inch $\times 10^{-3}$

Length No.	Cast No. 1	Length No.	Cast No. 5
1	38.2	1	38.5
2	36.6	2	40.0
3	38.6	3	39.8

Length No.	Cast No. 2	Length No.	Cast No. 6
1	36.8	1	37.6
2	37.1	2	38.2
3	36.4	3	37.6

Length No.	Cast No. 3	Length No.	Cast No. 7
1	38.4	1	36.7
2	37.7	2	38.2
3	36.8	3	38.7

Length No.	Cast No. 4	Length No.	Cast No. 8
1	38.6	1	37.4
2	37.9	2	38.0
3	37.8	3	39.2

Source: Excerpt from testing records, used with permission of Aluminum Company of Canada, Ltd.

Note: Lb./(square inch $\times 10^{-3}$) is known colloquially as "kips."

JUMBO COLA COMPANY (A)

Statistical Analysis of Bottling Lines,
Using a Group-control Chart

In producing bottled drinks, one of the characteristics requiring daily control is sugar content. A quick method of testing for sugar content is by means of a hydrometer. The hydrometer scale, by indicating specific gravity, provides an indirect measure of sugar content.

TABLE II-4. SUGAR CONTENT OF COLA DRINKS

Hydrometer Test Results in Degrees Brix,
Three Daily Tests per Bottling Line

Date of Test	Bottling Line 1			Bottling Line 2			Bottling Line 3		
	Test 1	Test 2	Test 3	Test 1	Test 2	Test 3	Test 1	Test 2	Test 3
Oct. 2	11.9	11.6	11.7	11.6	11.8	11.9	11.8	11.9	11.6
3	11.6	11.7	11.8	11.6	11.7	11.9	11.7	11.9	11.6
4	11.8	11.6	11 7	11.8	11.6	11.7	11.7	11.8	11.6
5	11.7	11.9	11.8	11.6	11.7	11.1	11.7	11.8	11.6
6	11.8	11.9	11.7	11.8	11.7	11.9	11.9	11.8	11.7
9	11.5	11.9	11.6	11 6	11.8	11.7	11.7	11.6	11.8
10	11.8	11.6	12.0	11.9	11.8	11.7	11.7	11.7	11.6
11	11.6	11.9	11.7	11.6	11.5	11.9	11.9	11.6	11.5
12	11.8	12.0	11.7	12.0	11.6	11.7	11.7	12.0	11.8
13	11.6	11.8	11.7	11.7	11.6	11.9	11.9	11.7	11.6
16	12.0	11.7	11.8	12.0	11.7	11.8	11.7	11.9	12.0
17	11.6	11.9	11.7	11.7	11.6	11.8	11.8	11.7	11.6
18	11.6	11.7	11.8	11.8	11.9	11.7	11.9	11.8	11.9
19	12.0	11.7	11.8	11.9	11.6	11.7	11.8	11.7	11.8
20	11.6	11.9	11.8	11.8	11.6	11.7	11.7	11.8	11.6
23	11.9	11.6	11.8	11.7	12.0	11.8	11.8	11.7	12.0
24	11.7	11.9	11.8	11.8	11.6	11.9	11.9	11.8	11.6
25	11.6	11.7	11.8	11.6	11.8	11.9	11.8	11.9	11.6
26	11.7	11.9	11.8	11.9	11.8	11.7	11.8	11.7	11.9
27	11.6	12.0	11.8	11.8	11.6	11.7	11.7	11.8	11.6

Test Total
Test Average
Line Average

Source: Control laboratory records.

A popular hydrometer scale is the Brix scale, developed by A. T. W. Brix (1798-1890), which expresses specific gravity of liquids at 15.6 degrees Centigrade in the following form:

$$\text{Specific Gravity} = 400/(400 + \text{Brix})$$

Hydrometer test results on three bottling lines are shown in Table II-4.

QUESTIONS

Plot and evaluate the fluctuations in averages in each line by means of statistical control charts (using 3-sigma limits) or by a single group control chart.

AEROSTREAM CORPORATION

Analysis of Purchase Requisitions, Using Occurrence-per-Unit, or C-charts

When using purchase requisitions in conjunction with an automated purchase-order processing system, it is essential that requisition forms be filled out fully and properly. Failure on the part of requisitioning personnel to comply with the form's requirements can lead to costly delays, since the computer section must then check back with the persons concerned, regarding missing or erroneous entries on the form. At other times, when an error is not caught in time, problems may arise after the material, parts, or supplies have been ordered, or when they are received, or later in actual production.

As part of a general administrative paperwork control system, one hundred requisitions were selected at random and checked each week. The results of this check are shown in Table II-5. A "defect," or faulty entry, would be concerned with an omission or an unreadable or erroneous entry on a requisition form.

Error could arise with regard to all sections of the form, particularly the part number and name, price quotation and date, buyer, material code, lead time, vendor name and number, shipping instructions, packaging specifications, quantities, terms, and other designations pertinent to adequate purchase requisitioning.

QUESTIONS

Evaluate the data by means of control charts for the various types of defects found, including the total weekly defects. Next, prepare

TABLE II-5. ANALYSIS OF PURCHASE REQUISITIONS

Week Numbers	Defects Found in Samples of 100 Requisitions			
	Omissions	Errors	Unreadable*	Total
1	1	0	1	2
2	3	0	2	5
3	1	1	0	2
4	8	2	3	13
5	2	0	0	2
6	0	1	1	2
7	6	2	2	10
8	2	1	0	3
9	0	0	1	1
10	4	1	4	9
11	4	1	3	8
12	1	0	0	1
13	0	0	0	0
14	0	1	2	3
15	2	1	0	3
16	1	2	0	3
17	0	2	0	2
18	2	1	1	4
19	1	0	2	3
20	2	0	2	4
Total	40	16	24	80

* or poorly or ambiguously written.

recommendations for management concerning the control of deficiencies in the preparation of purchase requisitions. Confine your report to 2 double-spaced pages and not more than 2 pages of exhibits.

MARCHANT DIVISION OF SMITH-CORONA MARCHANT, INCORPORATED

Control Chart for Rates and Percentages

Quality control records maintained by the Assembly department of Marchant, Division of Smith-Corona Marchant, Inc., revealed the following data on subassembly 32805, based on the first 8-hour shifts per day, during which approximately 1000 parts are used.

Date	Defective Parts Replaced, %	Number of Adjustments Required per Hour
10/3	1.5	30
4	1.3	25
5	1.7	31
6	2.2	40
7	2.0	38
10	2.5	56
11	2.6	32
12	2.3	50
13	2.4	46
14	5.0	70
17	3.0	40
18	2.0	38
19	1.8	27
20	2.2	28
21	2.3	46

QUESTIONS

As an aid to production management, in keeping parts replacements and mechanical adjustments at a minimum, calculate and prepare suitable control charts based on 3-sigma limits.

Once you have mastered correlation and regression analysis, you may also be asked to correlate the two series shown above.

BLACK CONSTRUCTION COMPANY

Control Chart for Building Specifications

Concrete specimens, collected daily from the construction of fallout shelters, have yielded the compressive strengths shown on page 37.

QUESTIONS

With the aid of a control chart based on 2-sigma limits, determine whether the contractor has met the minimum specification of 4000 pounds compressive strength per inch required for the particular types of shelters being built.

COMPRESSIVE STRENGTHS IN 100's OF POUNDS PER SQUARE INCH

Date	Specimen Number 1	2	3	4	5	Average	Range
1/2	46.0	43.5	43.1	47.3	45.1	45.00	4.2
1/3	45.0	45.7	40.9	44.0	43.6	43.84	2.1
1/4	42.0	47.3	44.5	45.6	48.0	45.48	6.0
1/5	49.1	45.7	46.4	46.0	47.1	46.86	3.4
1/6	47.1	44.2	49.6	45.1	47.4	46.68	5.4
1/9	43.1	44.4	43.4	45.8	46.4	44.62	3.3
1/10	41.2	45.5	45.9	46.5	43.8	44.58	7.3
1/11	41.0	46.7	43.3	49.4	48.0	45.68	8.4
1/12	45.4	43.7	47.3	44.8	49.2	46.08	5.5
1/13	40.0	43.1	48.3	44.5	46.7	45.72	5.2
1/16	45.2	46.7	47.3	47.1	49.8	47.22	4.6
1/17	44.2	43.5	45.0	44.0	44.7	44.28	1.5
Total						546.24	56.9
Average						45.5	4.7

SOUTHEASTERN TILE WORKS

Financial Management Charts

Douglas Lewis had recently been appointed assistant to the controller of Southeastern Tile Works, engaged in the production of plain and ornamental facing tile. Because of the highly competitive nature of the business, Doug felt that the company would benefit if management would accept and use a system of financial and administrative management control charts, of the type adopted by a number of firms in various industries in recent years.

Value of Financial and Administrative Management Control Charts

Doug's first job was to convince his superior, Mr. James Bullard, the controller. In addition to a discussion with Mr. Bullard, Doug prepared the following supplementary memorandum:

Statistical control charts are familiar and well-accepted quality surveillance aids in the modern plant. A relatively recent addition, adopted on the basis of success in other industries, are financial and administrative control charts for production and sales management. Such charts facilitate management control and management planning in four operational phases:

1. Past data and experience can be reviewed quickly in terms of past average performance and allowable fluctuations about this average.
2. Current data, representing current experience, may then be plotted and readily compared with past averages and variability from the average.
3. From this comparison, management will note quickly whether or not current performance is within the expected normal operating ranges. Moreover, any significant trends or developments will show up on the control chart.
4. Based on the information thus brought to management's attention, quick action can be directed towards those areas—be they labor cost, excessive waste, undesirable trends in controllable overhead, dangerous loss-rate of old customers, or other critical items—requiring management's concern, corrective steps, and follow-up. At the same time, those items which do not show undue changes—that is, actual performance is within the normally allowable range, as expressed by the control limits—do not call for any management attention.

While sound management has always involved procedures of the nature just outlined, the financial and administrative control charts simplify and enhance the effectiveness of management decision making. By bringing all pertinent data together in comprehensive and readily reviewable form, the control chart becomes also a time-saver. Some initial work is required in deciding what types of financial and administrative control charts are to be maintained, and arranging for the flow of data to permit routine plotting of the information. Once this has been accomplished, however, only two or three hours' clerical work per month are needed to keep the charts up to date."

Management by Exception

Doug's report continued as follows:

The financial and administrative control chart fits in well with the exception principle of management. This principle is built on the philosophy that there is an inherent amount of variability in any process, performance or costs series. This variability will be about the same tomorrow as it was yesterday, unless some definite or specific action or event has occurred to produce a change. Management should not be worried about or bothered by fluctuations in quality, costs or performance that stay within the range of variation that is normally to be expected. Only when a trend or sudden change should occur, indicative of a *significant* deviation above and beyond normally allowable fluctuations, is management attention and action required. With this philosophy, assurance is had that management time and energies are not needlessly spent, but are instead concentrated on those areas where real problems exist that require correction.

The criterion for distinguishing between normal variations and a significant trend or deviation is provided by the control limit of a control chart. Usually, there is an upper limit and a lower drawn a certain distance from the center line. A deviation beyond the limit, or a trend towards one of the limits, is indicative of developments requiring action.

Simple statistical procedures are available, using only elementary arithmetic, which may be used to develop control limits, based on the inherent variability exhibited by a series of data—be it costs, waste, efficiency or other types of figures. For financial and administrative control, limits based on so-called 95 percent confidence levels are generally desirable. So long as the actual plotted data fall within the control limits constructed on this basis, there is no need generally for management to be concerned. A plotted point falling outside the limits gives indication at the 95 percent level of confidence (or 5 percent risk of error) that a real change has occurred, requiring management's attention. Also, if no actual points have fallen outside the limits, but 4 or 5 points are consistently either above or below the center line, the trend thus evidenced provides a strong indication—again at the 95 percent confidence level—that something has changed in the process.

Managers generally act on the basis of the exception principle; and the control chart gives them a sharper dividing line between the considerations of "no action needed" and "attention required," thus aiding management in making these types of decisions in production, quality, and cost and sales problems.

Illustrative Charts

Next, Doug prepared a set of illustrative charts for financial and managerial control, as shown in Figures II-2 and II-3, using data obtained from the company's past performance records.

Using the illustrative control charts as examples, he sought to

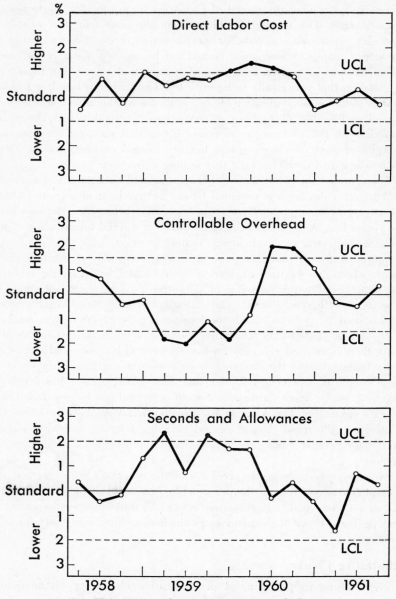

Fig. II-2. Financial management control charts
. . . Successive quarters . . .

o = Quarterly cost   . = Out-of-control
UCL = Upper control limit   LCL = Lower control limit

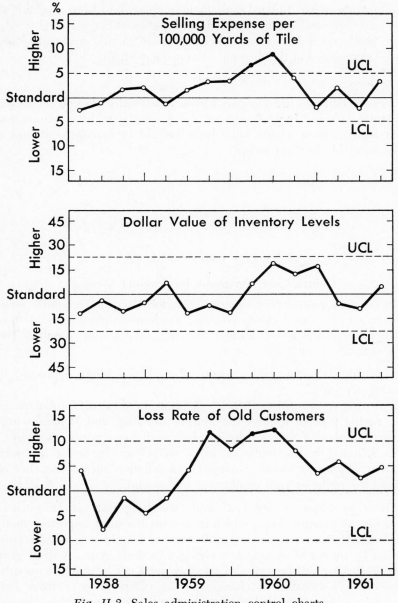

Fig. II-3. Sales administration control charts
. . . Successive quarters . . .

o = Quarterly cost   ● = Out-of-control
UCL = Upper control limit   LCL = Lower control limit

demonstrate to Mr. Bullard how, if these charts had been available in the past, financial, administrative, and policy decisions might have been made on a better basis, because more factual material would have been placed at the disposal of management.

QUESTIONS

Assume that you are Douglas Lewis. What value do you see in the illustrative charts? In what manner, specifically, would the information contained in these charts have been helpful to management had it been available in chart form?

UNISPIN YARN MILL (A)

Control-chart Programs for Product Weight

In order to control processing quality, the Unispin Yarn Mill maintains a set of control charts covering random-sampling tests in their three essential processes: finisher drawing, roving, and spinning. The following test results are shown:

1. Finisher drawing tests, results of stock weighings, expressed in "grains per yard."

2. Roving tests, results of stock weighings, in terms of "hank roving." The roving process follows the finisher drawing, and "hank roving" means "number of 840-yard lengths comprising one pound of strand."

3. Spinning tests, results of stock weighings, in terms of "yarn number." Spinning follows roving. "Yarn number" means "number of 840-yard lengths of yarn comprising one pound."

The expressions "sizing test" and "weighing test" are frequently used for this control check, which represents the most important quality-control test in a spun-yarn mill. Size or weight is generally controlled by means of appropriate changes in draft gears. A draft gear that is working satisfactorily on one day need not be suitable on subsequent days, because of changes in the composition of stock fed, variations in humidity and temperature, and because of other factors.

QUESTIONS

Using the data in Tables II-6–8 for the three important processes of

TABLE II-6. CONTROL CHART DATA, FINISHER DRAWING
(Sizing Test Results, Grains Per Yard)

Frame No.	17	21	22	23	24	25	26	Room Average
				September 1				
	53.0	52.8	53.2	51.0	52.0	52.2	51.8	
	53.0	53.6	53.2	53.2	53.8	53.0	53.6	
	53.2	51.4	52.0	53.2	52.2	53.2	52.6	
	54.0	53.6	52.2	53.2	53.2	53.6	52.8	
Total	213.2	211.4	210.6	210.6	211.2	212.0	210.8	
Average	53.30	52.85	52.65	52.65	52.80	53.00	52.70	52.85
Range	1.0	2.2	1.2	2.2	1.8	1.4	1.8	
				September 2				
Frame No.	17	21	22	23	24	25	26*	
	51.4	51.2	52.2	51.4	52.0	52.0	51.8	
	52.8	53.6	53.8	52.8	52.8	52.0	54.0	
	52.0	52.2	51.8	52.2	52.2	52.6	52.2	
	52.6	53.2	51.8	52.6	53.0	53.4	53.4	
Total	208.8	210.2	209.6	209.0	210.0	210.0	211.4	
Average	52.20	52.55	52.40	52.25	52.50	52.50	52.85	52.46
Range	1.4	2.4	2.0	1.4	1.0	1.4	2.2	
				September 3				
Frame No.	17*	21	22	23	24	25	26*	
	52.2	52.8	52.2	52.2	52.2	52.6	51.6	
	54.0	53.4	52.8	52.6	52.2	53.8	52.8	
	53.0	52.0	52.8	52.2	53.4	52.8	52.2	
	53.8	53.4	53.4	52.0	53.8	53.8	52.8	
Total	213.0	211.6	211.2	209.0	211.6	213.0	209.4	
Average	53.25	52.90	52.80	52.25	52.90	53.25	52.35	52.81
Range	1.8	1.4	1.2	0.6	1.6	1.2	1.2	
				September 4				
Frame No.	17	21	22	23	24	25	26	
	51.8	52.8	51.4	53.6	52.8	52.4	53.4	
	54.0	52.8	53.6	53.6	52.8	52.4	54.0	
	51.6	51.8	51.6	50.6	51.4	53.0	52.2	
	52.6	52.0	52.4	52.2	52.4	53.8	53.6	
Total	210.0	209.4	209.0	210.0	209.4	211.6	213.2	
Average	52.50	52.35	52.25	52.50	52.35	52.90	53.30	52.59
Range	2.4	1.0	2.2	3.0	1.4	1.4	1.8	

TABLE II-6. (Continued)

September 5

Frame No.	17	21	22*	23	22	25	26*	Room Average
	53.0	52.4	52.2	52.6	52.6	52.2	53.6	
	53.6	52.0	53.0	52.6	52.6	52.2	52.6	
	51.4	53.0	52.2	52.2	51.6	52.2	53.4	
	53.2	52.2	54.0	52.8	52.2	52.4	52.4	
Total	211.2	209.6	211.4	210.2	209.0	209.0	212.0	
Average	52.80	52.40	52.85	52.55	52.25	52.25	53.00	52.59
Range	2.2	1.0	1 8	0.6	1.0	0.2	1.2	

September 6

Frame No.	17	21	22	23	24	25	26	
	52.6	52.2	53.2	52.4	52.8	53.8	52.8	
	54.0	53.8	54.0	52.8	54.0	53.8	53.4	
	53.8	54.0	53.2	53.0	51.6	52.6	54.0	
	54.4	54.0	53.4	54.8	53.8	54.0	54.0	
Total	214.8	214.0	213.8	213.0	212.2	214.2	214.2	
Average	53.70	53.50	53.45	53.25	53.05	53.55	53.55	53.44
Range	1.8	1.8	0.8	2.4	2.4	1.4	1.2	

September 8

Frame No.	17	21	22	23	24	25	26	
	52.4	53.0	51.6	51.8	52.2	52.2	53.0	
	53.6	53.0	52.6	53.0	53.8	53.0	53.0	
	52.0	52.0	52.6	52.2	52.2	53.2	52.0	
	52.4	52.6	52.8	53.0	53.8	53.4	53.2	
Total	210.4	210.6	209.6	210.0	212.0	211.8	211.2	
Average	52.60	52.65	52.40	52.50	53.00	52.95	52.80	52.70
Range	1.6	1.0	1.2	1.2	1.6	1.2	1.2	

September 9

Frame No.	17	21	22	23	24	25	26	
	52.8	52.0	52.2	51.8	53.6	53.2	52.0	
	54.0	52.4	53.2	52.4	52.6	54.0	53.2	
	52.0	53.0	51.0	53.0	52.8	51.8	52.2	
	53.8	53.2	53.6	53.6	53.4	53.0	52.2	
Total	212.6	210.6	210.0	210.8	212.4	212.0	209.6	
Average	53.15	52.65	52.50	52.70	53.10	53.00	52.40	52.79
Range	2.0	1.2	2.6	1.8	1.0	2.2	1.2	

TABLE II-6. (Continued)

September 10

Frame No.	17	21	22	23	24	25	26	Room Average
	52.2	51.4	52.8	51.6	53.8	51.8	51.0	
	52.8	53.0	53.6	53.4	53.4	52.2	52.8	
	52.8	53.2	53.4	51.6	52.4	52.8	51.8	
	52.8	53.4	53.4	52.4	53.4	53.4	53.2	
Total	210.6	211.0	213.2	209.0	213.0	210.2	208.8	
Average	52.65	52.75	53.30	52.25	53.25	52.55	52.20	52.71
Range	0.6	2.0	0.8	1.8	1.4	1.6	2.2	

September 11

Frame No.	17	21*	22	23*	24	25	26*	
	52.8	53.8	52.0	52.6	52.2	51.8	52.0	
	53.2	53.8	52.2	53.6	52.2	52.6	52.8	
	51.8	52.6	52.2	53.2	52.6	52.2	53.0	
	53.6	52.8	52.6	53.2	52.8	52.8	54.0	
Total	211.4	213.0	209.0	212.6	209.8	209.4	211.8	
Average	52.85	53.25	52.25	53.15	52.45	52.35	52.95	52.75
Range	1.8	1.2	0.6	1.0	0.6	1.0	2.0	

September 12

Frame No.	17	21	22	23*	24	25	26*	
	53.6	53.2	51.0	52.8	5.32	52.0	52.2	
	53.6	53.4	53.6	53.4	53.2	53.0	52.4	
	53.0	53.8	52.0	52.6	52.2	53.6	52.0	
	53.2	54.4	52.8	53.8	53.4	53.6	53.4	
Total	213.4	214.8	209.4	212.6	212.0	212.2	210.0	
Average	53.35	53.70	52.35	53.15	53.00	53.05	52.50	53.01
Range	0.6	1.2	2.6	1.2	1.2	1.6	1.4	

September 13

Frame No.	17	21	22	23	24	25	26	
	52.8	51.8	51.0	53.0	52.4	52.4	51.8	
	52.4	52.6	51.8	53.2	53.0	53.8	52.8	
	52.8	53.2	51.8	52.6	52.2	53.0	52.0	
	52.8	53.6	54.8	53.0	53.2	53.0	52.4	
Total	210.8	211.2	209.4	211.8	210.8	212.2	209.0	
Average	52.70	52.80	52.35	52.95	52.70	53.05	52.25	52.69
Range	0.4	1.8	3.8	0.6	1.0	1.4	1.0	

TABLE II-6. (Continued)

September 15

Frame No.	17	21	22	23	24	25	26	Room Average
	53.4	52.2	52.4	52.4	51.6	53.0	53.6	
	53.8	52.6	54.0	52.8	53.2	53.0	54.0	
	53.0	54.0	52.0	52.2	53.4	53.6	53.2	
	54.4	54.6	54.0	53.6	53.4	54.6	53.6	
Total	214.6	213.4	212.4	211.0	211.6	214.2	214.4	
Average	53.65	53.35	53.10	52.75	52.90	53.55	53.60	53.27
Range	1.4	2.4	2.0	1.4	1.8	1.6	0.8	

September 16

Frame No.	17	21	22	23	24	25	26	
	53.6	51.4	51.6	52.2	51.8	52.8	52.0	
	54.0	52.0	53.2	52.4	53.6	53.0	52.6	
	52.0	52.4	52.6	52.0	51.8	53.6	53.0	
	52.8	53.8	54.6	52 6	52.6	54.6	54.0	
Total	212.4	209.6	212.0	209.2	209.8	214.0	211.6	
Average	53.10	52.40	53.00	52.30	52.45	53.50	52.90	52.81
Range	2.0	2.4	3.0	0.6	1.8	1.8	2.0	

* Gear changed previous day.

SUMMARY OF DATA

1. Total of finisher drawing test averages (ΣX)........ 5176.25
2. Number of test averages (N)...................... 98
3. Average grains per yard = (1) ÷ (2) or $(\Sigma X/N)$.... 52.8
4. Average range, R.............................. 1.529

TABLE II-7.　CONTROL CHART DATA, ROVING

Date Frame No.	9-1 27	9-2 35	9-3 3	9-4 11	9-5 21	9-6 9	9-8 32
	3.13	2.98	2.98	2.94	2.90	3.03	3.00
	3.18	2.88	2.90	2.90	3.00	3.05	2.85
	3.20	3.10	2.94	2.95	2.70	2.98	3.00
	3.24	2.90	3.08	2.94	3.05	3.11	2.95
Hank Roving	3.16	2.80	3.04	2.89	2.85	3.20	3.04
	3.12	2.99	2.97	2.99	2.86	2.96	2.97
	3.13	3.05	2.90	2.99	2.89	2.97	3.06
	3.20	3.01	2.88	2.89	2.90	3.07	3.15
	3.18	2.95	2.96	2.94	3.10	3.00	3.01
	3.24	2.98	2.95	2.97	3.00	2.95	2.98
Total	31.78	29.64	29.60	29.40	29.25	30.32	30.01
Average	3.178	2.964	2.960	2.940	2.925	3.032	3.001
Range	0.12	0.30	0.20	0.10	0.40	0.25	0.30
Date Frame No.	9-9 4	9-10 16	9-11 6	9-12 24	9-13 31	9-15 19	9-16 5
	2.96	3.02	2.97	3.03	3.05	2.97	2.97
	3.05	2.99	2.91	2.85	3.06	2.85	2.94
	3.00	3.15	2.98	2.98	3.00	2.90	3.04
	3.04	3.20	2.94	2.97	3.11	3.22	2.89
Hank Roving	2.89	2.95	2.94	3.15	3.12	2.84	2.88
	2.96	2.95	2.97	3.10	3.15	3.10	2.90
	3.02	2.98	3.00	2.94	3.09	3.12	3.08
	2.87	2.98	3.00	2.80	3.04	2.98	2.93
	2.95	3.18	2.91	3.12	3.01	2.72	3.01
	2.94	3.04	2.90	3.00	3.12	2.95	2.98
Total	29.68	30.44	29.52	29.94	30.75	29.65	29.62
Average	2.968	3.044	2.952	2.994	3.075	2.965	2.962
Range	0.18	0.25	0.10	0.35	0.15	0.50	0.20

TABLE II-7. CONTROL CHART DATA, ROVING (Continued)

Date Frame No.	9-17 2	9-18 30	9-19 17	9-20 29	9-22 14	9-23 8	9-24 25
	2.98	2.97	2.99	2.95	3.04	2.97	3.07
	3.08	3.01	2.91	3.15	2.99	3.01	3.02
	2.87	2.94	2.95	3.00	3.02	2.89	2.92
	2.90	2.95	2.98	2.75	3.01	3.00	3.04
Hank Roving	3.01	3.02	3.08	3.10	2.99	3.07	3.10
	3.06	2.98	3.00	3.11	2.96	2.94	3.00
	2.90	3.01	3.07	2.84	3.11	2.95	3.22
	2.97	2.95	3.05	2.85	2.98	2.91	3.10
	2.90	2.92	2.99	2.86	3.05	2.98	3.12
	3.06	3.00	2.91	2.90	3.08	2.87	3.15
Total	29.73	29.75	29.93	29.51	30.23	29.59	30.74
Average	2.973	2.975	2.993	2.951	3.023	2.959	3.074
Range	0.21	0.10	0.17	0.40	0.15	0.20	0.30

SUMMARY OF DATA

1. Total of roving size test averages (ΣX)............... 629.08
2. Number of test averages (N)........................ 21
3. Average hank roving = (1) ÷ (2) or ($\Sigma X/N$)........ 3.00
4. Average range, $\overline{R}$................................. 0.235

TABLE II-8. CONTROL CHART DATA, SPINNING SIZING TESTS

Date Frame No.	9-1 17	9-2 2	9-3 9	9-4 6	9-5 3	9-6 19	9-8 13
	38.5	40.0	37.8	37.1	34.3	37.1	38.4
	40.3	37.4	36.3	36.2	34.1	39.0	36.9
	35.4	40.0	38.8	36.2	37.0	35.8	37.3
	38.2	37.1	36.2	39.4	39.5	36.1	40.1
	41.6	39.5	38.0	38.2	37.3	37.2	39.5
Yarn No.	37.2	40.0	37.5	36.6	35.0	36.5	39.5
	39.8	36.2	38.2	39.1	36.6	37.5	38.8
	40.1	37.1	36.1	38.1	38.2	39.0	39.3
	40.1	40.0	36.0	36.2	36.0	38.2	37.9
	36.5	37.0	38.0	36.5	36.2	37.8	38.3
Total	387.7	384.3	372.9	373.6	364.2	374.2	386.0
Average	38.77	38.43	37.29	37.36	36.42	37.42	38.60
Range	6.2	3.8	2.8	3.2	5.4	3.2	3 2

Date Frame No.	9-9 5	9-10 21	9-11 16	9-12 20	9-13 4	9-15 7	9-16 15
	38.0	37.8	39.4	37.5	36.8	37.5	37.5
	37.5	39.2	38.5	37.2	35.4	35.5	36.0
	39.2	38.3	39.0	38.4	34.0	36.3	37.2
	38.3	38.5	40.5	39.1	38.2	38.5	38.1
Yarn No.	38.1	36.9	41.0	37.1	38.5	37.4	35.5
	39.0	36.8	38.4	36.9	37.5	39.7	39.0
	37.9	37.4	39.3	37.0	34.0	38.8	36.9
	38.2	39.0	38.9	38.0	36.5	37.5	37.0
	37.0	37.0	39.7	36.4	37.5	38.3	38.2
	36.8	37.0	39.5	38.1	34.0	37.9	39.5
Total	380.0	377.9	394.2	375.7	362.4	377.4	374.9
Average	38.00	37.79	39.42	37.57	36.24	37.74	37.49
Range	2.4	2.4	2.6	2.7	4.5	4.2	4.0

Date Frame No.	9-17 18	9-18 8	9-19 1	9-20 10	9-22 12	9-23 11	9-24 14
	37.5	38.2	38.0	38 7	37.9	37.5	37.1
	36.0	37.5	36.6	37.3	38.3	36.9	36.6
	37.2	39.3	36.0	38.4	38.5	36.4	38.4
	38.1	36.4	37.5	37.5	39.4	37.5	38.6
Yarn No.	35.5	39.4	38.2	37.9	38.0	38.4	39.2
	39.0	36.6	39.4	39.1	37.9	38.2	37.6
	36.9	39.8	37.0	39.3	37.9	37.0	38.0
	37.0	37.8	40.3	39.1	38.1	38.5	39.6
	38.2	38.5	38.4	38.6	39.7	38.4	39.1
	39.5	38.0	37.2	39.0	38.0	37.7	38.0
Total	374.9	381.5	378.6	384.9	383.7	376.5	382.2
Average	37.49	38.15	37.86	38.49	38.37	37.65	38.22
Range	4.0	3.4	4.3	2.0	1.8	2.1	3.0

SUMMARY OF DATA

1. Total of sizing test averages (ΣX) 7947.7
2. Number of test averages (N) 21
3. Average yarn no. = (1) ÷ (2) or $(\Sigma X)/N$ 37.8
4. Average range, $\bar{R}$ 3.39

finisher drawing, roving, and spinning sizing tests, prepare control charts. From the control charts, write a report to the mill manager, not over 500 words long, reporting the results of your control-chart analysis. You may assume that the mill manager is familiar with the purpose of control charts.

Chapter *III*

SIGNIFICANCE TESTS FOR SIMPLE COMPARISONS AND CHI-SQUARE

VIRGINIA COUNCIL OF HIGHWAY INVESTIGATION AND RESEARCH

Significance of Difference in Average-rupture Modulus of Two Concrete Mixes

Fly ash for power plants is cheap and has a pozzolanic (insoluble compound-forming) reaction with the free lime in a concrete mix. Previous success has been claimed for substitution of fly ash for part of the cement content in a mix, since fly ash increases workability, thus permitting a drier mix.

Using careful control, 16 3 × 3 × 16-inch test beams were made, one half with no substitution and the other half with 20 percent substitution. Observed flexural strengths at 28 days appear on page 51.

QUESTIONS

Would you consider the difference observed to be statistically significant, and if so, at what confidence level?

50

MODULUS OF RUPTURE

No Substitution		20% Substitution	
	910	975	
	895	950	
	960 (High)	925	
	925	986 (High)	
	885 (Low)	920 (Low)	
	955	921	
	933	956	
	929	967	
Average	924	948.5	
Difference			24.5
Range	885–960	920-985	

DRAYTON DETERGENT SERVICE

Significance of Difference between Two Averages in Evaluating Consumer Preference

Drayton Detergent Service was founded in the middle forties and was then engaged primarily in supplying soaps, detergents, antiseptics, polishing waxes, lubricating oils, and other similar products to large offices, buildings, and factories in a medium-to-large-sized metropolitan area.

Through the years, sales increased, and while the company originally purchased its products, it was now manufacturing and bottling many of them. A few years ago, Drayton began to market a consumer product, a liquid dishwashing detergent, which was advertised within the area and had a fair degree of acceptance.

Marketing Problem

Management was taking steps to modernize the packaging of the dishwashing liquid by changing from a metal to a plastic container. The metal container had been two-colored, blue and white, with black lettering. The plastic bottle proposed would, for reasons of technology and economy, have to be one color only.

In order to stay as close to the color scheme as that by which the public had come to know the product, the Sales department of Drayton decided that either a blue opaque or a white opaque plastic bottle should be used. A container of attractive design was developed, and pilot quantities of each color were purchased.

Survey

Ten grocery stores, located in various areas, were selected, who agreed to stock the new containers. Five stores carried the blue bottles, while the other five carried the white bottles. It was noted that the new plastic bottles had considerably greater sales than the old containers, and there was also some difference between the blue and the white plastic, as shown by Table III-1.

TABLE III-1.   SALES OF LIQUID DETERGENT

Gallons Sold, in 100's

Week No.	Blue Plastic	White Plastic
1	6.4	7.2
2	6.5	6.8
3	6.3	6.5
4	6.1	6.7
5	6.9	6.8
6	6.3	6.7
7	6.9	7.2
8	6.2	7.4
9	6.1	7.0
10	6.3	6.7
Total	64.0	69.0
Average	6.4	6.9

Significance Test

It was realized that the company would have to standardize one color for mass production. The pilot study indicated a consumer preference for the white bottle.

Before adopting the white bottle, the sales manager desired to know whether the higher sales volume observed during the sample study was statistically significant.

Questions

Prepare the significance test needed.

CLEARMOUNT MILLS

Significance of Difference in Various Comparisons in an Industrial Health Project

The productive efficiency and morale of workers is affected considerably by their state of health. Realizing this, the management of a Southern cotton mill, which we shall designate as "Clearmount," cooperated with two medical research workers, Drs. C. B. McKerrow and R. S. F. Schilling, of the Pneumoconiosis Research Unit, Cardiff, Cambridge, and the London School of Hygiene and Tropical Medicine, assisted by a grant from the Nuffield Foundation, in a study of the incidence of byssinosis in their mill.[1]

Epidemiology

Byssinosis is a lung impairment occurring in some persons after prolonged inhalation of cotton dust. In cotton mill workers, its most frequent symptom is chest tightness and breathlessness on returning to work after absence, such as after a two day weekend or a vacation.

Epidemiological data show that byssinosis represents a serious problem in the United Kingdom, as noted from Table III-2. In the United

TABLE III-2.   BYSSINOSIS IN ENGLAND AND WALES

Years	Recorded Deaths	Disability Pensions*
1942-44	14	20
1945-47	17	19
1948-50	26	124
1951-53	49	157
1954-56	84	428
1957-59	122	910

* New cases recorded.

Source: Annual Reports of Ministry of Pensions and National Insurance of Great Britain and Annual Reports of Chief Inspector of Factories, Great Britain.

States, no comparable records are available, but the evidence there is indicates that byssinosis is much less of a problem. Although the etiology of byssinosis is obscure, it is generally believed that lower

[1] Case data taken from the published research work of Drs. C. B. McKerrow, Cambridge, and R. S. F. Schilling, London, as given in the source references herein.

rates of incidents of the disease are associated with reduced amounts of cotton dust. Since the card room in a mill is usually the most dust laden, the incidence of byssinosis should be higher there than in any other processing department. It has also been shown that exposure to cotton dust in mills with a high prevalence of byssinosis is associated with a diminution in indirect maximum breathing capacity and an increase in airways resistance during the day's work. The changes appear to be due to a specific action of inhaled cotton dust and are not found among workers in mills spinning other fibers or among coal miners, who are exposed to much higher concentrations of dust.

Industrial Implications

It seems clear from a viewpoint of productivity that even in a mill that has never experienced a single instance of serious byssinosis, a moderate number of relatively light cases will mean that some degree of decreased vitality, strength, efficiency, and morale will be experienced by the operators affected. Thus, if a certain degree of actual byssinosis is established in a mill, it will be desirable for management to investigate possible remedial measures, such as:

1. Incorporation of special tests in purchasing raw stock, to avoid cottons containing excessive proportions of short fibers, which tend to add to card room "fly."
2. Addition of expensive dust-removal equipment, if warranted.
3. Further training of operators in the use of practices that tend to minimize unnecessary fly.
4. Transfer out of the card room to less dusty areas, wherever early byssinosis symptoms seem to warrant this.

These types of remedial action are, of course, not only expensive but also involve changes in operating practices that may be burdensome to personnel. For these reasons, large-scale changes would seem warranted only if a significant byssinosis incidence can be demonstrated in a mill.

Dust Sampling

Dust concentrations were measured with a Hexhlet device, which was connected to an appropriate suction pump, with dust intake coming from between two carding engines. For each test, the dust collected was weighed and the result was related to the known constant air-flow rate through the sampler. From six such samples, a mean concentration of 247 mg. per 100 cubic meters was found, which is considerably below the figure of 440 mg. observed in 105 English mills, but is nevertheless above the maximum level proposed by S. A. Roach and R. S. F. Schilling.[2]

Study of Workers

From the 232 persons in the card room and 2590 persons in other work rooms of the mill, 19 and 24 men respectively from the day shift, chosen by the personnel director on the basis of their long service in the mill, participated in the survey. They were not selected for any reason directly connected with their health.

Each participant filled out a questionnaire concerning frequency of coughs, production of phlegm, effect of weather on the chest, recent and previous illnesses, and smoking habits. The results are summarized in Table III-3.

TABLE III-3.   CHEST SYMPTOMS AMONG WORKERS

	Card Room		Other Departments*	
	Smokers	Nonsmokers	Smokers	Nonsmokers
No. of Workers Tested	11	8	11	18
Mean Age, yr.	48	44	44	39
No. of Symptoms per Worker**	2.6	1.5	1.6	1.0

* Spinning, winding, and weaving.
** Includes persistent cough or phlegm, wheezing, chest tightness, and chest affected by weather.

Source: C. B. Kerrow and R. S. F. Schilling, "A Pilot Enquiry into Two Cotton Mills in the United States," *J. of Am. Med. Assoc.*, Vol. 177, No. 12, Sept. 23, 1961, 850-853.

The volume of air expired over the first 0.75 seconds of a forced expiration from full expiration (Forced Expiratory Volume, F.E.V., 0.75) was measured, and the averages of three such determinations per worker, at the start and end of each shift, are reproduced in Table III-4.

[2] "Clinical and Environmental Study of Byssinosis in Lancashire Cotton Industry," in the *British Journal of Industrial Medicine*, Vol. 17, Jan., 1960, pp. 1-9.

TABLE III-4.   FORCED EXPIRATORY VOLUME IN MALE CARD-ROOM
WORKERS AND OTHERS DURING A SHIFT

	Male Card-Room Workers (F.E.V./Liter)				Other Male Workers (F.E.V./Liter)		
Subject	Morn-ing	After-noon	Change	Subject	Morn-ing	After-noon	Change
1	3.02	3.00	−0.02	18	2.48	2.50	+0.02
2	3.50	3.43	−0.07	19	3.81	3.74	−0.07
3	2.90	2.11	−0.79	20	4.41	4.36	−0.05
4	3.48	3.25	−0.23	21	2.13	2.26	+0.13
5	3.60	3.63	+0.03	22	3.64	3.58	−0.06
6	4.00	3.80	−0.20	23	3.84	3.64	−0.20
7	3.81	3.68	−0.13	24	3.33	2.90	−0.43
8	3.46	3.38	−0.08	25	3.42	3.23	−0.19
9	3.88	3.64	−0.24	26	2.48	2.40	−0.08
10	3.04	2.82	−0.22	27	3.73	3.54	−0.19
11	2.62	2.04	−0.58	28	3.97	4.16	+0.19
12	2.91	2.45	−0.46	29	3.50	3.39	−0.11
13	2.59	2.41	−0.18	30	2.60	2.67	+0.07
14	2.88	2.71	−0.17	31	3.65	3.53	−0.12
15	3.40	3.47	+0.07	32	2.26	2.13	−0.13
16	2.84	2.63	−0.21	33	3.97	3.96	−0.01
17	3.07	2.74	−0.33	34	3.59	3.57	−0.02
				35	3.40	3.10	−0.30
Mean	3.24	3.01	−0.22	Mean	3.35	3.26	−0.09

Evaluation

From the data in Tables III-3 and III-4, it appears that:

1. Card-room workers have a higher number of chest symptoms than other workers in the mill.

2. Smokers have a higher number of chest symptoms than non-smokers.

3. There is a drop in forced expiratory volume between morning and afternoon readings for both groups of workers, and the loss is more than twice as great for the card-room group than for the other male workers.

Before any definite conclusions are formed, however, the observations should be subjected to statistical significance tests. These tests cannot, of course, overcome a distinct flaw in the balancing of the experimental conditions, apparent from a review of Table III-3. In drawing conclusions, this flaw plus any other possible deficiencies must be considered.

The evaluation should be presented to management in concise and complete manner, in order to facilitate review and decisions.

QUESTIONS

Prepare the analyses and evaluations needed.

BENNETT PUMP DIVISION

Significance of Difference between Two Averages and Two
Standard Deviations in Statistical Process Engineering
for Fuel-pump Production

The Bennett Pump Division of John Wood Company manufactures gasoline fuel pumps noted for the quality of their design and construction. A special feature of the pumps is the all-metal four-piston meter, capable of handling any fuel that can be marketed for use in modern cars. Craftsmanship, dependable performance, and low maintenance costs were stressed in the development, production, and sale of the pumps.

As part of a continuing program of process and product improvement, the process engineering group was investigating the desirability of a new pneumatic positive torque screw wrench for use in assembling the meter covers to the meter bodies. Existing practice had been to use a pneumatic impact wrench, the action of which is affected by dwell time. The positive torque wrench, however, is not affected by dwell time. It was believed, therefore, that the positive torque wrench would result in more uniform torque readings on bolts, when assembling the meter cover to the meter body.

In view of the engineering factors involved, processing specifications called for a torque reading on bolts of 6-foot pounds with a plus and minus tolerance of 2-foot pounds. A cap screw, Part No. A-970, was used in the assembly.

Production Testing

In order to evaluate the new positive torque wrench, tests were made on the production floor, based on an operator's use of both the new wrench and the standard impact wrench, shown in Tables III-5 and III-6.

TABLE III–5. SECURING OF COVER TO METER BODY, USING STANDARD PNEUMATIC IMPACT WRENCH

Torque Readings on Bolts in Foot Pounds

January 5
Cap Screw Position

2	3	1	4
4	5	7	7
5	4	6	5
6	9	3	8
6	3	5	6

January 9
Cap Screw Position

3	2	4	1
5	4	6	8
10	6	7	3
7	5	6	10
5	9	7	6

January 17
Cap Screw Position

1	4	3	2
4	7	4	7
3	7	5	8
3	4	6	7
3	7	4	8

January 20
Cap Screw Position

4	2	1	3
7	8	8	5
4	7	4	8
7	7	6	5
8	8	7	4

January 24
Cap Screw Position

3	1	2	4
8	7	6	7
8	4	5	6
9	5	4	6
5	4	6	9

January 31
Cap Screw Position

2	1	3	4
3	3	5	5
3	2	6	6
8	5	4	5
3	4	4	7

Assembly involves the securing of 4 meter covers, one for each of the 4 piston cavities. A cover is secured by 10 cap screws, so that a total of 40 cap screws is used for each meter body. The critical areas tested were the first 4 cap screws put down with the wrench at the start of the bolt pattern. These are subject to slight change when the pressures of all 10 cap screws are exerted on the cork gasket. On each piston cavity cover, the critical positions for the first four cap screws were labeled 1, 2, 3, and 4 in successive order, so that position 1, for example, represents the same location on each cover.

On each date shown in the tables, one meter head assembly was tested, using cap screw positions 1, 2, 3, and 4 in the order indicated. For example, in Table III-6, on January 5, the first cover tested yielded a torque reading of 6 foot pounds for position 2, 8 foot pounds for position 1, 7 foot pounds for position 4, and 5 foot pounds for position 3. The next cover had torque readings of 4, 6, 7, and 4 for positions 2, 1, 4, and 3 respectively.

TABLE III–6. SECURING OF COVER TO METER BODY,
USING POSITIVE TORQUE PNEUMATIC SCREW WRENCH

Torque Readings on Bolts in Foot Pounds

January 5					January 9			
Cap Screw Position					**Cap Screw Position**			
2	**1**	**4**	**3**		**2**	**4**	**1**	**3**
6	8	7	5		7	6	7	6
4	6	7	4		4	3	5	6
6	3	6	7		6	5	8	7
4	6	8	6		5	7	6	6

January 17					January 20			
Cap Screw Position					**Cap Screw Position**			
3	**4**	**1**	**2**		**1**	**2**	**3**	**4**
7	6	5	6		6	7	6	7
7	6	7	5		7	7	8	6
7	7	8	6		6	7	8	6
7	7	6	7		6	7	7	8

January 24					January 31			
Cap Screw Position					**Cap Screw Position**			
2	**1**	**3**	**4**		**4**	**2**	**1**	**3**
6	6	7	6		7	6	6	8
5	8	7	8		6	5	6	6
8	7	7	7		7	6	5	6
7	7	6	8		8	6	5	7

Engineering Factors

The following engineering factors are pertinent to the assembly operation:

1. When bolts have a torque tightness of 9 foot pounds or more, distortion of the cover occurs, causing leakage of gasoline between the cover and the body of the meter.

2. When bolts have a torque tightness of 3 foot pounds or less, leakage occurs between the cover and the gasket.

3. When bolts are not secured to a torque tightness of at least 4 foot pounds, leakage complaints from the field are reported after the pump has been placed in service for a relatively short period of time.

4. There is a slightly higher tooling cost for the positive torque wrench, since it requires more frequent repair than a standard impact wrench. This cost, however, is less per annum than the average cost of three service calls on leakage complaints under the pump warranty.

It is thus evident that proper torque tightness of bolts is important for pump quality and avoidance of leakage complaints.

QUESTIONS

Analyze the given data and present your conclusions and recommendations.

BARBER-COLMAN COMPANY

Using Chi-square in Development Engineering to Compare Performance of New versus Existing Equipment

The development engineer was reviewing data on the quality of output of a new production machine, as compared with the past experience on an existing machine, as follows:

Quality Grade of Machine Output Obtained	Pieces of Each Grade Produced	
	Existing Machine	New Machine
Top Grade	200	227
High	400	376
Medium	300	330
Low Grade	100	67

The quality data for the existing machines represented an average rate per 1000 pieces obtained from the past year's records, while the data for the new machine represented an actual run of 1000 pieces under conditions considered equivalent to those encountered in normal production.

Although the new machine tended to show better quality, the development engineer was aware that the data were based on a relatively limited amount of actual production and that there are chance fluctuations in machine performance. He desired a statistical confidence level of 99 percent (risk of 1 percent) that the new machine was actually superior and that his observations were not ascribable to chance fluctuations of sampling. He therefore asked the mathematician to evaluate the data and to present his statistical conclusions.

QUESTIONS

You are asked to do the mathematician's job.

UNICOAT PROCESSING COMPANY

Evolutionary Operation (Evop)

The Unicoat Processing Company is engaged in plastic coating of various materials, such as paper, nonwovens, and other products. A particular highly sensitive paper must be coated with a minimum of impurities, and it is believed that finisher roll pressures in processing and viscosity (in centipoise, C. P.) of batch mix have an important effect on the formation of impurities on the surface of the coated material.

An investigation, using the modern techniques of "evolutionary operation" was made, using the arrangement shown in Figure III-1, with resultant outcomes as shown in Table III-7.

TABLE III-7. PERCENT IMPURITIES OBTAINED FROM 5 PROCESSING SETUPS, USING 4 TEST CYCLES FOR EACH SETUP

Processing Setup Used*	Testing Cycle**				Results	
	I	II	III	IV	Average	Range
1	0.93	0.96	0.96	0.95	0.95	0.03
2	.98	.97	.96	.93	.96	.05
3	.92	.93	.92	.91	.92	.02
4	.93	.95	.92	.96	.94	.04
5	.94	.98	.92	.96	.95	.06
Total					4.72	0.20
Grand Average	4.72/5				0.944	
Average Range	0.20/5					0.04

* Each setup involved a different combination of finisher roll pressure and batch viscosity, as identified from the systematic arrangement shown in Figure III-1.
** Each testing cycle consisted of 50 rolls per processing setup. Data shown represent the percent impurities.

QUESTIONS

As leader of the evop-team of the plant, prepare the following material:

1. An analysis of the results and a statistical significance evaluation.
2. Recommendations for the next suggested evop setup.
3. A possible expansion of the investigation to include also the effect of dresser roll pressures (suitable dresser roll pressures range from 10

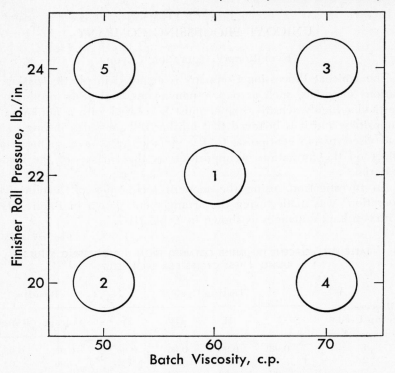

Fig. III-1. Design of investigation, comparing existing processing setup 1 against setups 2 through 5

to 20 pounds per square inch). For effectiveness, support your presentation with graphs wherever possible.

BRISTOL LABORATORIES, INCORPORATED (B)

Chi-square Analysis of Sampling Procedures

In the drawing of laboratory samples from penicillin fermenters, the avoidance of contamination is of considerable importance.

It was desired to investigate the difference in the occurrence of contamination between samples drawn by (1) production operators and (2) laboratory technicians.

From a record of the number of fermenters harvested during a 2-months' period and the number of samples presumed to be contaminated because of extreme variation between in-process and harvest-assay results, the data below were obtained:

Number of Samples

Sampled by	Contaminated	Uncontaminated	Total
Technicians	17	157	174
Operators	56	240	296
Total	73	397	470

QUESTIONS

Analyze these data and then indicate how management could use the information to reduce the incidence of contaminated samples.

MAYO CLINIC

Chi-square Analysis of Chest–X-ray Survey

It is generally recognized in the medical profession that the reading of chest X-rays will involve a certain (small) proportion of errors even by the most expert. In order to investigate these matters further, a study was made by Drs. Joseph Berkson, C. Allan Good, David D. Carr, and Andre J. Bruwer of the sections of biometry and medical statistics, roentgenology and medicine, Mayo Clinic, Rochester, Minnesota, to estimate the reliability of reading chest films, especially of patients referred for roentgenographic study in the course of medical examination at the clinic.

Objective

The rationale and method of the study was set forth as follows:

The objective was limited to the designation of a roentgenogram as "positive" or "negative." "Positive" means the presence of a shadow indicating a pathologic condition of the lung; "negative" means the absence of such a shadow. The conception is that there are roentgenograms which, if studied with sufficient care by competent roentgenologists, will be found to be "positive." Such roentgenograms may be read erroneously by a particular roentgenologist, but, if the pathologic shadow is indicated to him, he will agree on the positivity.

Of course, in reality, there are roentgenograms that do not conform to this conception. No matter how carefully they are studied, by an individual roentgenologist or by several in consultation, complete agreement will not result—some will definitely consider the roentgenogram positive, some negative. Such roentgenograms are considered "doubtful" and are not included in this study. The object of the present investigation is to ascertain the reliability of the reading of such "positives" and "negatives" when this is done in the usual manner of viewing a large number of roentgenograms successively as a diagnostic aid in clinical practice.

Results

Five hundred roentgenograms were presented in random arrangement to each of 9 readers, 5 of whom were roentgenologists and 4 of whom were specialists in diseases of the chest. Of the 500 X-rays, 98 had previously been identified as "positive" and 402 as "negative."

The same X-rays were next presented in a new random order and read as stereoscopic roentgenograms. (The single, nonstereoscopic

TABLE III-8.   COMPARISON OF READINGS OF SINGLE AND
STEREOSCOPIC ROENTGENOGRAMS

	False Negative, Percent			False Positive, Percent		
	Reading Roentgenogram			Reading Roentgenogram		
Reader	Single	Stereo-scopic	Difference	Single	Stereo-scopic	Difference
A	13.3	14.3	+1.0	3.0	2.5	−0.5
B	29.6	8.2	−21.4	1.0	0.5	−0.5
C	19.4	19.4	0.0	1.7	0.2	−1.5
D	18.4	18.4	0.0	1.2	0.7	−0.5
E	22.4	22.4	0.0	2.5	0.7	−1.8
F	12.2	5.1	−7.1	1.7	0.7	−1.0
G	19.4	11.2	−8.2	0.5	0.5	0.0
H	18.4	23.5	+5.1	6.7	3.5	−3.2
I	13.3	11.2	−2.1	12.2	13.2	−1.0
Mean	18.5	14.9	−3.6	3.4	2.5	−0.9

roentgenograms in the first set represented in each instance one plate from the pair used for stereoscopic X-rays.) From the results, as summarized in Table III-8, an improvement in reliability is noted for use of stereoscopic roentgenograms.

QUESTIONS

Assume that you are preparing a report favoring the use of (the more expensive) stereoscopic chest films in a large medical school and hospital, prepare a chi-square test of significance on the Mayo Clinic data to support your recommendations.

Chapter *IV*

ANALYSIS OF VARIANCE IN PRODUCTION, MARKETING, AND RESEARCH

INDUSTRIAL RESEARCH CORPORATION

Two-factor Variance Analysis

The data in Table IV-1 represent the maintenance experience on three similar electronic computers rented by Industrial Research Corporation.

TABLE IV-1. COMPUTER MAINTENANCE EXPERIENCE

Number of Repairs Required per Month,
by Time of Day, over a 1-Year Period

| Time of Day | Computer Number | | | | |
From To	1	2	3	Total	Average
8:00–9:59 AM	2	1	3	6	2.00
10:00–11:59 AM	4	7	1	12	4.00
12N–1:59 PM	2	8	9	19	6.33
2:00–5:00 PM	4	8	3	15	5.00
Total	12	24	16	52	
Average	3	6	4		4.33

Note: Basic entries rounded for purpose of simplification.

66

It appears that computer no. 1 has the lowest repair rate, while computer no. 2 has the highest rate. Moreover, breakdowns requiring repair tend to reach a peak during the first part of the afternoon.

QUESTIONS

How would you test the validity of these conclusions?

ARMOUR RESEARCH FOUNDATION (A)

Two-factor Variance Analysis with Replication

Assume that you have used the dust-particle counter (discussed in the Armour Research Foundation Case B), and have observed the results shown in Table IV-2, in checking the air in a white room.

TABLE IV-2. CONTAMINATION PARTICLE COUNTS PER HOUR BY SAMPLING STATIONS AND SHIFTS. TWO TESTS PER SHIFT

Item	Shifts	Test No.	Sampling Stations				Totals	Averages
			A	B	C	D		
	I	1	2	1	3	2		
		2	1	7	1	3		
Totals			3	8	4	5	20	
Averages			1.5	4.0	2.0	2.5		2.50
	II	1	3	9	9	3		
		2	1	8	3	0		
Totals			4	17	12	3	36	
Averages			2 0	8.5	6.0	1.5		4.50
	III	1	3	7	2	0		
		2	2	8	6	4		
Totals			5	15	8	4	32	
Averages			2.5	7.5	4.0	2.0		4.00
Column Totals			12	40	24	12	88	
Column Averages			2.00	6.67	4.00	2.00		3.67*

* Grand average of particle counts.

QUESTIONS

Analyze the results and present your findings.

UNISPIN YARN MILL (B)

Variance Analysis of Product Strength, Nested Classification

When customers complained about a deterioration in the quality of the no. 30 knitting yarn, causing excessive strand breakage in the knitting machines, it seemed apparent that weak yarns were causing the trouble. Yet, a review of the past four weeks' testing records, as shown in Table IV-3, showed that the average strength was 49.46 pounds, which conforms to general industry standards and does not represent a deterioration compared to prior months.

TABLE IV-3. TENSILE STRENGTHS IN POUNDS OF 6 BOBBINS
RANDOMLY SAMPLED FROM EACH SPINNING FRAME

Machine No.	August 1				August 8			
	10	74	57	60	8	45	2	46
	49.0	49.0	48.0	48.0	49.0	50.0	56.4	51.0
	46.3	44.0	49.5	46.0	51.0	51.0	56.0	47.5
	46.5	46.5	48.0	49.0	50.0	50.1	54.0	53.2
	49.0	47.5	47.0	48.0	50.0	50.0	53.5	47.0
	46.0	50.0	50.0	47.0	50.0	50.1	58.4	50.6
	49.5	47.0	49.0	50.0	50.0	49.5	56.0	53.0
Average	47.8	47.3	48.6	48.0	50.0	50.2	55.7	50.4
Machine No.	August 15				August 22			
	7	43	34	48	80	49	18	14
	50.0	48 3	54.5	48.0	48.0	50.0	47.0	45.0
	50.0	52.0	50.3	49.5	46.5	51.5	47.0	46.0
	49.2	48.7	48.0	49.5	49.5	51.2	47.0	48.0
	51.6	49.7	49.0	49.0	48.0	52.0	45.0	47.5
	48.6	51.4	53.0	48.5	48.5	52.0	47.5	49.0
	49.0	52.7	52.0	49.0	46.5	52.0	45.0	48.5
Average	49.7	50.5	51.2	48.9	47.8	51.5	46.4	47.3

On each day shown above, the 4 frames tested were selected randomly.
From routine mill-testing record.

A check of the tensile testing machine, operator testing procedures, sampling methods, and temperature and humidity controls revealed nothing wrong, so that the test data could be accepted as accurate.

Visual examination of the data raised the suspicion that there may be excessive variation in yarn strength. Such excessive variation could cause undue breakage during knitting.

QUESTIONS

Review Table IV-3, using appropriate statistical analysis techniques, and write a report advising management of the most likely source of excessive variation, as evidenced by the information at hand.

Confine your report to not more than 1 single-spaced page of text and not more than 2 pages of tabular or graphic material.

LAWRENCEVILLE DISTILLING COMPANY (A)[1]

Analysis of Variance in Alcohol-yield Evaluation

Application of new strains of yeast and improved fermentation practices has increased the yield of yeast in Lawrenceville Distilling Company's Fermenter Rooms A and B. Moreover, a prior observed difference in average yield between fermenter rooms had been practically eliminated. As a means of still further enhancing yield, two new organic additives, X and Y, for inhibiting the growth of contaminating bacteria, were being tried on several randomly selected fermenters in each room. The results are shown below:

ALCOHOL YIELD WITH TWO BACTERIOSTATIC ADDITIVES

Fermenter Room A			Fermenter Room B		
Fermenter No.	Additive X	Y	Fermenter No.	Additive X	Y
3	7.2	7.4	4	7.0	7.4
8	7.0	7.2	7	6.7	7.0
12	6.9	7.1	14	7.5	7.2
26	7.3	7.5	20	7.2	7.6

[1] Further information on Lawrenceville is contained in the B case (page 107), but is not needed for the present problem. The B case refers to a problem that had been solved by management before the investigation for the A case was begun.

QUESTIONS

What conclusions would be drawn from the alcohol yields, in percent, shown?

Confine your report to 1 page (no graphs).

MOWEN'S DEPARTMENT STORE

Factorial Analysis of Credit-collection Methods

The writing of "past due" notices and follow-up letters is always a problem in credit management, since a strongly worded letter may alienate customer goodwill, while a weak letter may not receive the attention that it deserves. In such situations, much depends on the skill of the letter writer.

Collection Letter

Recognizing these ramifications, Mr. Stuart Morris, customer service manager of the Mowen Department Store, was reviewing the forms of the final payment request, and was considering using the following possible measures before turning seriously delinquent accounts over to a collection agency:

1. Phone call, followed up by a diplomatic but firm letter, including self-addressed reply envelope, with meter stamp.

2. Diplomatic but firm letter, including self-addressed reply envelope, with meter stamp.

3. Diplomatic but firm letter, including self-addressed reply envelope, but requiring postage stamp.

4. Letter, as in 2, but on embossed blue letterhead with the caption in red: "An Urgent Appeal from the Customer Service Manager Concerning Your Account!"

Mr. Morris would have liked to consider a variety of possible wordings, but the presently used "diplomatic but firm" design had required a great deal of consultation, some years ago, with the merchandising managers, the store manager, and the owner. Mr. Morris did not propose to change this wording, which had been agreed to by all parties concerned. He did, however, receive approval to try first, second, and fourth approaches listed above, which were new methods, while (3) was the form that had been customary in the past.

Sampling and Results

Using a table of random numbers, a decision was made on each seriously delinquent account, and one of the four forms of collection request was then used. The percentage of accounts that responded within 10 days with full or partial payment or definite promise of early future payment is shown in Table IV-4.

TABLE IV-4.   EFFECTIVENESS OF FOUR COLLECTION METHODS

Percentage of Successful Responses

Amount Due, $	Month	Collection Method				Total	Average
		1	2	3	4		
up to 99	Feb.	42.2	37.8	33.4	40.5		
	Mar.	41.7	37.5	33.8	42.3		
	Total	83.9	75.3	67.2	82.8	309.2	
	Average	42.0	37.6	33.6	41.4		38.65
100-200	Feb.	42.2	36.7	34.2	40.1		
	Mar.	41.5	36.2	33.7	42.1		
	Total	83.7	72.9	67.9	82.2	306.7	
	Average	41.8	36.4	34.0	41.1		38.34
Over 200	Feb.	43.9	36.5	35.8	39.2		
	Mar.	41.3	36.6	35.4	40.3		
	Total	85.2	73.1	71.2	79.5	309.0	
	Average	42.6	36.6	35.6	39.8		38.62
Total		252.8	221.3	206.3	244.5	924.9	
Average		42.13	36.88	34.38	40.75		38.54

It was noted that method 1 gave the best results, but it was also the most time-consuming approach. Method 3 appeared to be the least expensive but also the least effective.

Analysis

Before standardizing the approach to use in future collection activities, Mr. Morris desired to evaluate the sampling results. He was particularly interested in (1) the significance of difference in percentages of response to each collection method and (2) the effect of the size of the amount owed on response to each collection method (interaction).

From these analyses, Mr. Morris could then make further decisions.

QUESTIONS

Prepare a brief analysis for Mr. Morris, with specific regard to his two interests.

CARTWRIGHT DISTRIBUTORS

Latin-square Design in Evaluating Advertising Effectiveness

Cartwright Distributors is a wholly owned selling and distributing organization for Cartwright Brewers, Inc.

In evaluating the effectiveness of 4 proposed advertisng display posters, differing primarily by the girl used in the picture, a trial test

TABLE IV-5. MASTERBREW BEER SALES

Number of Kegs per Week per Each of 20 Selected Bars per Section

Pairs of Week Nos.	Section of City				Total	Average
	North	South	East	West		
1 and 7	A:54	B:29	C: 71	D:44	198	49.5
3 and 6	B:59	A:22	D:100	C:22	203	50.8
2 and 5	C:40	D:38	B: 79	A:31	188	47.0
4 and 8	D:83	C:29	A:100	B:27	239	59.8
Total	236	118	350	124	828	
Average	59.0	29.5	87.5	31.0		51.8

Summary by Advertising Displays*

	A	B	C	D
Total	207	194	162	265
Average	51.8	48.5	40.5	66.3

* Advertising displays placed within bars differed by picture of girl used, as follows: A, blonde; B, auburn; C, redhead; D, brunette.

was made by displaying different girls' pictures on posters in different bars, using the arrangements shown in Table IV-5.

QUESTIONS

Review the results and determine whether there is adequate evidence to (1) permit standardizing on *one* city-wide display poster as best from an overall viewpoint *or* (2) justify the extra expense of using different posters for different sections.

How does this example emphasize the need for balanced design in market research investigations?

PRECISIONEER MACHINE SHOPS

Multifactor Experimentation

Precisioneer Machine Shops had developed an improved spinning frame for synthetic staple. Several spinners had expressed willingness to obtain a trial frame for evaluation purposes. It was felt by the company, however, that before sending out these trial frames, instructions as to the best processing settings should be provided, so as to insure proper use of the frames. Otherwise, if a spinner used settings that would not be suitable, the new frame might not yield good quality and would thus be rejected, with the consequent loss of a large order.

From industry experience it was known that the predominant yarn count spun was a 40's count, and the most comprehensive test was evenness, as measured on an electronic instrument, giving direct readings in "variation coefficient." Other yarn characteristics, such as strength, were related to evenness, so that a more even yarn would also be expected to be a stronger yarn.

After careful planning, a processing experiment was performed using several levels of those processing variables considered most important—roving twist, roving size, and spinning break draft. The test results are given in Table IV-6 and are graphed in Figure IV-1.

QUESTIONS

Perform a variance analysis; be prepared to discuss your findings and conclusions.

TABLE IV-6. VARIATION COEFFICIENTS OBTAINED WITH VARIOUS ROVING SIZES,
ROVING TWISTS, AND BREAK DRAFTS

Roving Size	Roving Twist	Spinning Break Draft				Total	Average
		1.4	1.6	1.8	2.0		
1.00	0.6	17	16	17	17	67	16.6
	0.7	16	16	17	17	66	16.5
	0.8	16	16	17	17	66	16.5
	0.9	16	16	17	17	66	16.5
Total		65	64	68	68	265	66.1
Average		16.3	16.0	17.0	17.0		16.5
1.10	0.6	18	16	17	16	67	16.6
	0.7	17	16	17	16	66	16.5
	0.8	16	15	17	16	64	16.0
	0.9	16	16	17	16	65	16.2
Total		67	63	68	64	262	65.3
Average		16.6	15.8	17.0	16.0		16.3
1.20	0.6	16	16	16	16	64	16.0
	0.7	15	16	16	16	63	15.8
	0.8	15	16	16	16	63	15.8
	0.9	16	16	16	16	64	16.0
Total		62	64	64	64	254	63.6
Average		15.5	16.0	16.0	16.0		15.9
1.30	0.6	16	16	17	17	66	16.5
	0.7	16	16	17	17	66	16.5
	0.8	15	16	17	17	65	16.3
	0.9	15	16	17	17	65	16.3
Total		62	64	68	68	262	65.6
Average		15.5	16.0	17.0	17.0		16.4

Notes
1. Roving size is measured in "number of 120-yard lengths of roving per pound."
2. Roving twist is measured in "turns per inch/ $\sqrt{\text{size}}$."
3. Draft is measured in "size produced/size fed."

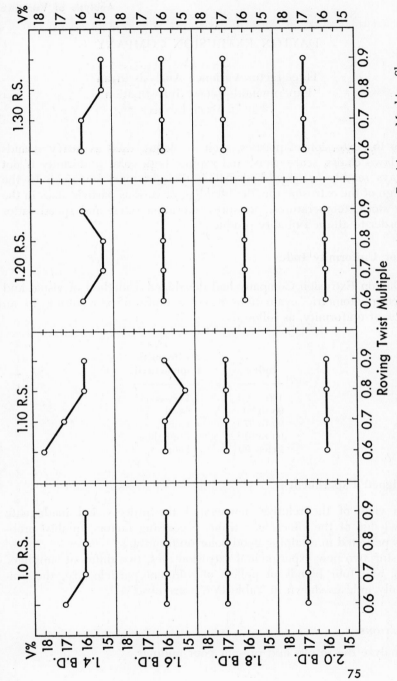

Fig. IV-1. Evenness variation coefficients (V%) obtained from multifactor experiment at Precisioneer Machine Shops

DAYTON EXTRUSION COMPANY

Three-factor Variance Analysis in an
Experimental-process Investigation
(2 by 2 by 4 Levels)

In the extrusion of plastics, such as olefins, used as heavy strands for lawn chairs, seat covers, and roping, high color uniformity is not always readily accomplished. Much thought must be given to the design of the extrusion die, the blending of various particle sizes in the raw stock, temperatures, pressures, vibration rates, and speed ratios in order to attain a quality product.

Color Uniformity Index

Dayton Extrusion Company had developed a method of visual and spectrophotometric evaluation of color uniformity, resulting in an index of uniformity, as follows:

Index	Uniformity Represented
100	Very good
98 to 99	Good
95 to 97	Fair
90 to 94	Borderline
Below 90	Poor

Designed Experiment

In view of the relative newness of the process and inadequate knowledge of the effects of various processing factors, quality problems persisted in attaining good color uniformity.

Using two new experimental extrusion dies, two different suppliers' dyes, and four blends of pellets of different particle size, the uniformity indexes shown in Table IV-7 were observed.

QUESTIONS

Analyze the results and present your findings.

TABLE IV-7. COLOR UNIFORMITY INDEXES OBSERVED WITH EXTRUSION EXPERIMENT
USING TWO DIES, TWO DYE SUPPLIERS, AND FOUR PELLET BLENDS

| | | Extrusion Dies | | | |
Suppliers	Blends	A	B	Blend Average	Supplier Average
Alpha Company	1	93	98	95.5	
	2	95	97	96.0	95.00
	3	92	96	94.0	
	4	96	93	94.5	
	Die Avg.	94	96		
Beta Company	1	92	94	93.0	
	2	93	95	94.0	94.25
	3	92	95	93.5	
	4	91	96	93.5	
	Die Avg.	92	95		

U. S. NAVAL ENGINEERING EXPERIMENT STATION

Latin-square Design in a Development-Research Study

With the increase in efficiency of underwater sound detection devices, the Navy was interested in developing a quiet power transmission. The accoustics Branch of the Wave Mechanics Laboratory of the Engineering Experiment Station was assigned the study of noise characteristics of various reduction-gear designs as one phase of this problem. The long-range program was concerned with gear material, geometry, and finish.

The possible extraneous factors present in this study, such as lubrication, operating conditions, method of measurements, and so forth, are so numerous that it was advisable to conduct a preliminary study to determine optimum operating conditions of test. The objective was to find the optimum lubricating conditions as regards gear-noise output. Specifically, the purpose was to determine the significance of input-lubricant temperature, rate of flow (in gallons per minute, gpm), and angle of impingement (inmesh and tangential each at top and bottom) under various conditions of speed (in revolutions per minute, rpm) and load (percent) as related to noise.

TABLE IV-8.   TEST DATA IN DECIBELS

	VOLUME															
Load and Speed	½ gpm Direction					1 gpm Direction					2 gpm Direction					Total
	TB	IT	IB	TT	Total	TB	IT	IB	TT	Total	TB	IT	IB	TT	Total	
25%			120°					90°					160°			
300 rpm	92.7	95.9	92.7	92.2		91.3	87.7	93.6	92.9		86.9	90.7	92.1	90.6		
1200 rpm	81.4	79.2	85.5	81.4	701.0	68.0	77.7	76.2	72.2	659.6	78.2	97.9	80.2	85.8	702.4	2063.0
100%			90°					160°					120°			
300 rpm	94.2	88.6	89.8	89.8		89.7	87.8	90.4	90.4		91.9	85.4	85.7	82.6		
1200 rpm	80.2	83.7	83.9	75.4	685.6	86.0	86.6	79.3	85.0	695.2	84.8	79.5	86.9	79.0	675.8	2056.6
125%			160°					120°					90°			
300 rpm	88.7	92.1	91.7	93.4		90.3	90.3	90.4	89.7		88.4	86.3	88.3	88.6		
1200 rpm	94.2	91.1	89.2	86.2	726.6	86.7	83.5	86.6	83.0	700.5	75.8	71.2	87.9	84.5	671.0	2098.1
Total			90° 2016.2		2113.2			TEMPERATURE 120° 2077.3		2055.3			160° 2124.2		2049.2	6217.7

Notes: First T = Tangential, Second T = Top, I = Inmesh and B = Bottom.

LOAD	VOLUME		
	1/2 GPM	1 GPM	2 GPM
25%	120°	Tangent-Bottom 300 rpm Inmesh-Top 1200 rpm Inmesh-Bottom 300 rpm Inmesh-Top 300 rpm Tangent-Top 1200 rpm Tangent-Top 300 rpm Tangent-Bottom 1200 rpm Inmesh-Bottom 1200 rpm 90°	160°
100%	90°	160°	120°
125%	160°	120°	90°

Fig. IV-2. Schematic of Latin-Square design

Discussion between the engineers and the statisticians, Mrs. Besse B. Day Mauss and Mr. F. R. Del Priore, resulted in the 3 × 3 Latin-square design with split plots as shown in Figure IV-2.

The test data obtained, in decibels, are given in Table IV-8.

QUESTIONS

Analyze the results and summarize your findings.

BRISTOL LABORATORIES, INCORPORATED (C)

Statistical Tolerancing in Filling Pharmaceutical Vials

In the filling of a 10-cc. vial with a relatively viscous injectable suspension, it was necessary to assure 10 separate 1-cc. injections. In such a situation, it is necessary to provide more than 10 cc. of the pharmaceutical in the vial, since the physician using the vial will not draw exactly the same amount each time, and he may end up with only ½ cc. for his tenth injection.

Variables Involved

A study of the problem revealed the following major sources of variability:

1. *Syringe holdup.* The residual amount of material remaining in the syringe which averages 0.2 cc. and the variability between syringes, with a standard deviation of 0.005 cc.

2. *Vial holdup.* The residual amount of material that cannot be withdrawn from the vial, which averages 0.5 cc., with a vial-to-vial standard deviation of 0.04 cc.

3. *Filling equipment.* Equipment variability in filling the vial was measured to represent a standard deviation of 0.03 cc.

QUESTIONS

The problem is to develop specifications for the average amount of material to be filled into each vial, so as to assure at the customary 3-sigma limits that the physician will actually obtain 10 injections of 1 cc. each from the vial.

LAKE CHARLES CHEMICAL COMPANY

Combination of Variance Components in the Analysis of Oxidation Efficiency

Efficiency of ammonia oxidation in a nitric acid plant is estimated on the basis of the percentage of ammonia in the inlet gas ($\%NH_3$) converted to nitric oxide in the outlet gas ($\%NO$).

In particular, if efficiency in percent is designated by E, and if A is percent of ammonia in inlet gas and N is percent nitric acid in outlet gas, then

$$E = \frac{N(100 - 1.25A)}{A}$$

where 1.25 represents the ratio of ammonia to nitric oxide.

Standard deviations of testing variations, inherent in the chemical-analysis procedures, are 0.05% for ammonia and 0.1 percent for nitric oxide. The average percentages of ammonia and nitric oxide in the inlet and outlet gases are 13 and 15 percent respectively.

QUESTIONS

Estimate the limits, at the 95-percent confidence level, within which oxidation efficiency can be determined with the present analytical methods used at the plant.

UNIRENT LICENSING CORPORATION

Combination of Variance Components in Risk Evaluation

The Unirent Licensing Corporation sells exclusive franchises for health studios, utilizing the specialized exercising equipment developed and patented by the Corporation. A licensing agreement usually runs for three years and stipulates certain requirements regarding space, fixtures, personnel, and a standard fee of $50 per course of "unit" of 10 treatments charged per customer.

Income and cost statistics for the first year of operation in cities similar to the one in which you are considering acquiring a license are shown in Table IV-9.

TABLE IV-9. INCOME AND COST STATISTICS

Item	Symbol	Average	Standard Deviation
Quantity Sold, Units per Year	Q	5000	1000
Sales Price, $ per Unit	S	50*	0*
Selling Expense, $ per Unit	E	10	1
Advertising, $ per Unit	A	1	0.46
Fixed Costs, $ per Year	F	100,000	10,000
License, $ per Year	L	65,000	0

* Standard price, agreed on by all licensees when signing contract.

Notes
1. Income, $I = QS = 5000 \times \$50 = \$250,000$
2. Total Cost, $C = QE + QA + F + L = Q(E + A) + F + L$
   $= 5,000 (10 + 1) + 100,000 + 65,000 = \$220,000$
3. Profit, $P = I - C = 250,000 - 220,000 = \$30,000$

Source: Data obtained from similar licensed businesses in other cities of similar size, for the first year of operation.

QUESTIONS

Assuming that the data are reliable, and that the standard deviations shown are based on approximately normal distributions, what would be the probability or risk that in your first year of operation you would break even or have a loss?

In your calculations, assume that you have as much skill and luck as the average entrepreneur represented by the experience summarized in Table IV-9, and that there will be no major change in general business conditions.

Chapter *V*

REGRESSION AND CORRELATION

PIERRE PLAZA HOTEL

Regression Analysis in a Wage-administration Program
(Job Evaluation)

The Pierre Plaza is a large, first-rate hotel in a metropolitan area, catering primarily to businessmen, conventions, and vacationers. Recently, a consulting firm had been hired for the purpose of preparing job descriptions and evaluations for the mechanics, electricians, plumbers, bellboys, maids, doormen, mail clerks, night watchmen, kitchen help, and other hourly paid personnel at the hotel. For each type of job, the hourly pay rate and corresponding evaluated job points were determined as shown below:

Job	Hourly Pay, $	Job Evaluation Points	Job	Hourly Pay, $	Job Evaluation Points
A	1.30	200	L	2.80	500
B	1.20	230	M	2.90	530
C	1.40	240	N	3.10	580
D	2.00	300	O	3.00	490
E	1.30	210	P	2.10	280
F	1.60	310	Q	1.90	210
G	1.80	340	R	2.70	470
H	2.30	350	S	3.90	600
I	2.60	380	T	1.70	220
J	2.10	400	U	3.30	450
K	3.60	600	V	2.60	260

83

The consultants then reported on the following findings:

1. The degree to which actual hourly pay rates correlated with the evaluated job points.
2. Jobs that were overpaid and jobs that were underpaid, based on the evaluated job points.
3. Recommendations for a policy to gradually bring hourly pay to closer correlation with evaluated job points.

The consultants' report was supported by a graphic presentation of the findings.

QUESTIONS

Prepare the consultant's report, using no more than one graph and two typewritten pages.

JUMBO COLA COMPANY (B)

Regression Analysis of Cost Relationships

The head-office bottling plant of the Jumbo Cola Company, located in a large metropolitan center, was concerned with production and distribution costs, as shown by the breakdown of major categories below:

Cost Item	Percent
Raw Materials	55
Overhead	10
Distribution	20
Plant Labor	15

It was realized, however, that these costs varied with production rates, and that the most variable cost was the expenditure of plant labor. The cost account was asked to provide detailed data concerning these cost factors, as an aid to management in formulating plans and initiating policies leading to less variable and possibly lower costs.

The cost accountant tabulated the data shown in Table V-1, and in addition prepared two graphs showing the following approximate cost relationships:

1. For each production increase of 50,000 cases, output per man-hour increases by 1 case.
2. For each production decrease of 50,000 cases, output per man-hour decreases by 1 case.
3. Labor cost decreases an average of two cents per case for each production increase of 50,000 cases.

The tabulations and graphs were of considerable service in making improvements that led to more stable and generally lowered unit costs of production.

QUESTIONS

Prepare the two graphs, showing clearly the cost relationships inherent in the data in Table V-1.

TABLE V-1. LABOR COST DATA

Bottled Cola Production

Month	Actual Cases in 1000's			Cases Per Man-hour			Labor Cost per Case for 1961* Cents
	1959	1960	1961	1959	1960	1961	
January	157	103	73	6.3	4.0	4.7	13.1
February	158	95	74	6.0	4.0	4.2	13.0
March	190	107	85	7.1	5.2	5.1	12.5
April	219	109	91	8.0	5.1	4.7	12.2
May	213	113	107	7.5	4.6	5.6	11.8
June	250	131	140	8.1	5.8	6.4	10.0
July	278	133	135	9.0	6.3	6.0	10.3
August	325	131	144	9.3	5.8	5.3	10.1
September	225	111	96	7.3	5.0	5.4	12.3
October	157	92	94	5.3	4.5	4.0	12.2
November	118	90	82	4.3	5.5	4.6	12.4
December	122	87	87	4.3	4.3	4.2	12.7

* Only the 1961 labor cost is shown, since a change in pay rates makes the prior monetary figures non-comparable.

In addition, compute correlation coefficients, significance levels, and standard errors of estimate.

ARMOUR RESEARCH FOUNDATION (B)

Regression Analysis in
White-room Maintenance

In recent years, the development of devices with increasing sensitivity to contamination has been commonplace. Hydraulic control systems for aircraft and missiles, miniature relays, semiconductors, photographic film, pharmaceutical compounds, surgical dressings, the floated gyroscope, and high gain optical systems are examples of products that cannot function reliably if contaminated.

Particle Sizes

Particles normally found suspended in air cover the size and concentration ranges shown in Table V-2. In comparison to these particle

TABLE V-2. TYPICAL DUST LEVELS IN URBAN, RURAL, AND SHOP AIR

Particle Size Ranges	Concentration, Particles per Liter		
(Diameter, microns)	Urban	Rural	Shop
0.7 to 1.4	47,000	1250	75,000
1.4 to 2.8	4300	480	4000
2.8 to 5.6	1400	160	180
5.6 to 11.2	120	40	60
11.2 to 22.4	20	0	15

Source: Collection of dust particles gathered and analyzed by Armour Research Foundation.

sizes, clearances of less than one ten thousandth and surface finishes smoothed to less than two microinches are vital to satisfactory performance of many precision devices. The need for exclusion of particle contaminants has led to special assembly and test spaces, known as white rooms.

Present white-room designs have not yet solved all problems of contamination control, so that rejection rates attributable at least in part to contaminants are generally well over 10 percent.

Specifications

Specifications for the cleanliness, conditions, and performance of white rooms vary over a wide range. The following, however, represents a typical set of specifications for conditions of the air in the room:

Item Controlled	Specification	Tolerance
Air Temperature, °F	70	±1
Relative Humidity, %	40	±2
Pressure (in terms of H_2O above that of next zone)	0.1	
Particles per Cubic Foot		
a. 0.5 microns	10,000	
b. 10 microns	none	

In theory, if specifications are not met, the room is to be closed until corrections have been made. This is easily done with the first 3 specifications, but control of particle content is more difficult.

White-room Operation

An original investment of approximately a million dollars will usually provide a white room of 10,000 square feet in size, but annual maintenance costs of the room may well run twice as high as this investment. Yet, the more effectively the white room is kept clear of contaminants, the lower will be the cost of scrap and rework produced in the area.

As an aid in assuring white-room integrity, the Armour Research Foundation developed an automatic particle counter, designed to measure the extent of contamination in an area.

TABLE V-3. CONTAMINANT LEVEL AND WHITE-ROOM POPULATION

White-room Population (No. of Persons)	Contaminant Level (Particles/Liter)
2	80
4	220
5	380
7	370
9	570
12	480
13	700
14	720
32	1810
38	2190

Source: Data obtained by means of Armour Research Foundation automatic particle counter.

Using this particle counter, the data in Table V-3 were obtained. These data confirmed and reemphasized an important major cause of

88   *Regression and Correlation*

white-room contamination. The conclusions thus obtained were helpful to management in its continuing endeavors to perfect white-room
operations.

QUESTIONS

Perform an appropriate statistical analysis of the data in Table V-3
and present your conclusions to management.

BITUMINOUS LABORATORY

Evaluation of Surface Friction by Means of Regression and Correlation Analysis

Measurement of the coefficient of friction (C/F) of highway surfaces
is important, since a higher coefficient will generally mean a road of
less "slipperiness" and a shorter stopping distance when brakes must
be applied suddenly. The customary means of measuring friction
(method A) is to close off a section of highway and to run tests with
an automobile. Brakes are applied, and the distance for the car to
come to a stop is used in calculating the friction coefficient.

A simplified procedure (method B), which does not require closing
off the road for testing, involves the momentary locking and unlocking
of brakes, usually for a one second interval. The deceleration is measured on a decelerometer installed in the test vehicle, and the results
are converted to coefficient of friction.

Question Posed

The following question was posed to the research staff of the
Bituminous Laboratory of the Virginia Council of Highway Investigation and Research: Can the simplified method B be substituted
throughout the state for the more difficult, but theoretically correct,
method A?

Experimental Procedure

Measurements by the two methods, A and B, were made simultaneously, so that pairs of measurements were obtained on various
strips of Virginia highways. The research engineers assumed that the
2 most important factors under which the experiments should be
conducted constituted (1) levels of friction and (2) surface texture,

since the interacting effect of these two conditions would affect the measurements.

Since existing road surfaces had to be used, it was not possible to select ideal combinations of levels and surface textures. It was not possible, for example, to select a pavement that had both a low level of friction and a "coarse texture." The experimenters therefore selected the types of pavements that included "typical" pavements and also pavements that were widely divergent. The pavement selected, therefore, represented the range of surface textures and friction levels generally found in the state of Virginia. The results of the measurements are shown in Table V-4.

TABLE V-4. FRICTION COEFFICIENTS OBTAINED

Data in 0.01 C/F

Road Testing Site	Test Method	Test Number							Test Average	
		1	2	3	4	5	6	7	A	B
I	A	48	45	47	46	51	48	49	47.7	——
	B	44	41	45	47	50	47	53	——	45.3
II	A	61	62	61	61	62	64	—	61.8	——
	B	62	63	66	63	64	67	—	——	64.2
III	A	54	54	51	51	—	—	—	52.5	——
	B	53	54	55	54	—	—	—	——	54.0
IV	A	58	57	61	61	58	59	—	59.0	——
	B	60	57	64	61	63	64	—	——	61.5
V	A	57	59	56	57	58	56	58	57.3	——
	B	58	59	60	59	60	59	58	——	59.0
VI	A	57	57	57	58	59	57	58	57.6	——
	B	58	59	57	59	60	59	61	——	59.0
VII	A	52	53	55	52	53	—	—	53.0	——
	B	54	54	53	54	55	—	—	——	54.0
VIII	A	59	59	63	56	59	59	58	59.0	——
	B	58	60	59	55	63	53	59	——	58.1
IX	A	44	45	45	44	45	45	47	45.0	——
	B	43	43	43	42	42	43	42	——	42.6
X	A	57	58	58	55	—	—	—	57.0	——
	B	57	60	55	55	—	—	—	——	56.8
XI	A	63	59	61	62	62	67	68	63.1	——
	B	67	67	65	65	69	66	67	——	66.6
XII	A	40	40	38	39	42	41	39	39.9	——
	B	35	34	34	35	36	33	36	——	34.7

Total
Grand Average

— = No data obtained.   —— = Not applicable.

QUESTIONS

Evaluate the data found in relation to the question posed and state your conclusions.

BALL CONTROL IN FOOTBALL

Correlation Analysis

Football coaches have often said that the team that controls the ball is the team that will normally win. The term *control* refers to the maintaining of the ball on offense and is sometimes measured by the number of first downs that a team accumulates, since a team must relinquish the ball if it does not make a first down within four plays from the line of scrimmage.

On the other hand, the number of first downs may not necessarily reflect the score or the winner. Team A might control the ball by "marching" up and down the field throughout the game and thereby accumulate numerous first downs but be unable to get the ball across the goal line. Team B might score through long plays or nonscrimmage plays such as kick runbacks and thereby win without registering many first downs.

QUESTIONS

By using the statistics for the Rose-, Sugar-, Orange-, and Cotton-Bowl games played on January 1, 1962, let us determine the importance of ball control by measuring the relationship between each team's number of first downs and its score.

Bowl	Team	First Downs	Score
Rose	Minnesota	21	21
	U.C.L.A.	8	3
Sugar	Alabama	12	10
	Arkansas	7	3
Cotton	Texas	12	12
	Mississippi	17	7
Orange	L.S.U	19	25
	Colorado	7	7

CANTERBURY BISCUIT COMPANY

Multiple Correlation Analysis in Marketing

After a year of promotion of "Canterbar," a new ten-cent bar of chocolate biscuit, the sales manager was reviewing the progress made. Since this product represented the first entry of Canterbury into the candy-bar business, and financial resources were limited, promotion had been confined to medium-sized cities in the East and relied primarily on newspaper advertising.

Selecting 19 cities of similar character and size (20 to 25,000), the following data on promotional effort and results were available:

1. Monthly sales of "Canterbar" in thousands.
2. Dollar cost, per day, of advertising.
3. Days per year of salesmen's visits to the community (including fractional days).

The data are tabulated in Table V-5.

TABLE V-5. EFFECT OF NEWSPAPER ADVERTISING AND SALES VISITS
ON SALE OF CANTERBURY'S "CANTERBARS"

City	Monthly Sales in 1000's of Bars	Daily Advertising Cost, $	Salesmen's Visits per Year, Days
A	1.50	1.70	3.6
B	1.56	1.38	8.4
C	1.41	1.38	11.4
D	2.00	2.20	6.7
E	1.60	2.20	7.7
F	1.40	1.60	4.8
G	2.20	1.90	15.6
H	1.20	2.00	13.8
I	1.80	1.20	9.3
J	1.40	1.20	11.4
K	1.90	2.00	8.8
L	1.10	1.50	8.4
M	1.70	1.60	8.4
N	1.60	1.60	11.4
O	1.60	2.40	8.7
P	1.30	1.70	9.2
Q	2.00	1.60	11.0
R	2.10	3.20	15.0
S	1.50	1.60	16.0

In order to plan further promotional programs, the sales manager was reviewing the data to evaluate the relative effect of newspaper advertising and salesmen's visit days on sales of "Canterbar."

QUESTIONS

Prepare a multiple correlation analysis to aid in the sales manager's evaluation.

SPOTLESS LAUNDRY

Determination of Replacement Schedules to Minimize Total Cost, Using Regression Analysis and Incremental Analysis

The Spotless Laundry was evaluating a new type of pressboard cover for its shirt presses. Made of a synthetic material, the new cover lasted several weeks in place of the old cotton covers that stood up for only a few days. It was observed, however, that the new covers tended to harden and then crack and break buttons during pressing. The cost of replacing broken buttons was estimated at 5¢ per button. The cost of a press cover is $15. Experiments, investigating the relationship between button breakage and press-cover age, yielded the following data:

Cover Age, Days	Buttons Broken Per Day
40	85
45	83
50	90
55	93
60	95

Beyond 60 days, covers were generally not usable, since they would begin to split.

QUESTIONS

1. Prepare a correlation graph, including the regression line; then calculate the correlation coefficient and determine its significance.

2. After how many days should the cover be replaced in order to minimize costs?

TABLE V-6. RAILROAD STATISTICS

State	Miles of Road	Number of Employees	Annual Payrolls	State and Local taxes
Alabama	4 646	10 041	$ 63 000 000	$ 5 352 357
Arizona	2 184	4 841	30 000 000	6 930 404
Arkansas	3 872	8 650	54 000 000	3 827 622
California	7 630	47 476	298 000 000	27 176 817
Colorado	3 786	8 795	55 000 000	6 525 255
Connecticut	825	6 265	39 000 000	1 201 552
Delaware	293	2 538	16 000 000	201 993
Dist. of Col.	31	2 350	15 000 000	144 007
Florida	4 655	13 246	83 000 000	6 084 615
Georgia	5 854	15 356	96 000 000	5 793 531
Idaho	2 685	4 684	29 000 000	4 752 268
Illinois	11 201	69 401	435 000 000	32 131 313
Indiana	6 593	21 482	135 000 000	17 352 154
Iowa	8 561	13 269	83 000 000	7 873 259
Kansas	8 215	19 015	119 000 000	13 803 762
Kentucky	3 526	16 659	104 000 000	6 381 814
Louisiana	3 937	8 959	56 000 000	5 541 579
Maine	1 784	3 772	24 000 000	1 770 517
Maryland	1 141	13 576	85 000 000	3 992 007
Massachusetts	1 633	9 191	58 000 000	4 812 484
Michigan	6 640	20 255	127 000 000	8 938 027
Minnesota	8 174	22 988	144 000 000	12 461 145
Mississippi	3 659	4 595	29 000 000	3 716 728
Missouri	6 582	22 208	139 000 000	8 401 283
Montana	4 962	7 622	48 000 000	7 214 998
Nebraska	5 721	14 370	90 000 000	4 034 887
Nevada	1 647	2 215	14 000 000	2 367 544
New Hampshire	854	561	4 000 000	364 431
New Jersey	1 914	19 664	123 000 000	18 420 192
New Mexico	2 473	4 523	28 000 000	2 541 164
New York	6 463	54 406	341 000 000	39 932 326
North Carolina	4 310	7 940	50 000 000	5 284 982
North Dakota	5 194	4 738	30 000 000	5 577 255
Ohio	8 322	47 147	296 000 000	24 278 184
Oklahoma	5 777	5 307	33 000 000	6 946 211
Oregon	3 174	9 483	59 000 000	4 526 577
Pennsylvania	9 092	63 859	400 000 000	11 450 827
Rhode Island	181	1 110	7 000 000	1 162 032
South Carolina	3 284	4 426	28 000 000	3 280 123
South Dakota	3 920	1 735	11 000 000	1 428 161
Tennessee	3 402	13 467	84 000 000	9 023 429
Texas	14 755	34 976	219 000 000	8 817 634
Utah	1 736	6 418	40 000 000	4 154 998
Vermont	811	1 597	10 000 000	238 523
Virginia	4 113	20 263	127 000 000	13 514 344
Washington	4 987	12 980	81 000 000	5 560 172
West Virginia	3 681	13 196	83 000 000	11 465 112
Wisconsin	6 193	13 433	84 000 000	5 557 106
Wyoming	1 882	4 596	29 000 000	3 252 821

Source: Association of American Railroads, Bureau of Railway Economics, Report 132082, October 1961.

RAILROAD STATISTICS

Correlation between Economic Data

Railroads are the principal agency of commercial intercity freight transportation in the United States. They provide not only a basic transportation service but also participate to an important extent in local economic and business activities throughout the country.

The statistical information in Table V-6 is taken from Report 132082, October, 1961, by the Bureau of Railway Economics of the Association of American Railroads. Miles of road shown represent mileage owned by class I and II linehaul railroads and their affiliates, excluding 572 miles in Alaska and 25 miles in Hawaii. Other data shown in the table are for class I railroads only, which account for about 93 percent of all railroad employment and tax accruals and for 96 percent of total operating expenses of all railroads.

The number of employees is as of March 15, 1961. Payroll data are estimated on the basis of the level of employment existing on that date. Average Class I railroad employment over the year 1960 was 780,494 with a total payroll for wages and salaries of $4,893,558,158.

QUESTIONS

Analyze the data for correlation among the following relationships:

1. Miles of road and state and local taxes.
2. Number of employees and annual payrolls.
3. Combined effect of miles of road and number of employees on annual payroll.
4. Which railroads have significantly below-average payrolls and which have significantly above-average payrolls?

Chapter *VI*

SAMPLING IN PRODUCTION, ADMINISTRATION, AND DISTRIBUTION

CONSULTANT IN STATISTICAL SURVEYS

Responsibilities in Sampling Surveys

With increasing use of consultants in connection with statistical surveys for various business purposes, the problems concerning the professional requirements of conduct between the business organization and the consultant, and their mutual obligations, come to the forefront. The following is a "Code of Professional Conduct" that is submitted to prospective clients by W. Edwards Deming, noted statistical consultant. Only if this code is agreed to will Dr. Deming consent to work with the client. The code is interesting as a basis for discussion of the manifold aspects arising from consultant relationship in statistical surveys designed to meet the increasing requirements of business to obtain and have on hand valid and useful information as a basis for decision-making.

1. I aim to engage only in work that offers opportunity (a) to create improved statistical methods, or (b) to use new or existing statistical methods (i) to help other scientists and professional men to improve their methods and research; or (ii) to acquire new knowledge through planned research about materials and about men; or (iii) to improve efficiency, uniformity, quality, service, and performance of product; or (iv) to achieve smoother operation and more effective administration and management in industry and in government.

2. I make no solicitation for engagements, but depend on recommendations. Speeches and the publication of books, and of papers in professional and scientific journals, which explain new statistical techniques, or which explain to people in other professions, the various ways in which statistical work may be helpful to the public service toward the acquirement of new knowledge, and toward the achievement of more efficient production, smoother operation, and better performance, etc., are the duty of any statistician, and are not construed as solicitation for me personally.

3. An engagement with a client carries with it certain responsibilities, some mine, some the client's· This code will define some of these responsibilities. The reason for stating them explicitly is (a) to enable me to render better service; (b) to forestall disappointment on the part of the client, who if he fails to exercise his responsibilities in the planning of the survey or experiment, may not realize in the end its fullest possibilities, or may discover too late that certain uses that he intended to make of the results are impossible.

4. The client will state what his problem is and how he could use the results of a statistical investigation.

5. My responsibility in any engagement is only for its statistical aspects:

a. to assist the client to formulate his problem in statistical terms.

b. to explain to him the procedure, cost, and utility of various possible frames and of various feasible plans of sampling and of experimentation.

c. to design a sample of specified material, covered by the frame that the client certifies as satisfactory for study, to reach the precision that the client specifies in the formulation of his problem; or to design an experiment to reach significance in the tests of materials, methods, levels, types, and conditions that the client certifies are needful to study.

d. to explain to him that the results of any survey or experiment may be impaired if the proposed frame and experimental conditions that he certifies as satisfactory fail to include the entire range of materials, methods, levels, types, and conditions concerning which he desires information.

e. to explain to him that any objective inferences that one may draw from the results by statistical theory can only cover the frame and the methods, levels, types, materials, and conditions presented for study: that generalizations to other materials, methods, and conditions can be made only through knowledge of the subject-matter; that I can take no responsibility for such generalizations.

6. My instructions to the client will define the sampling units, and how to classify and number them in the frame. I will furnish the sampling table to draw the sample after the client certifies that the preparation of the frame, including the scheme for the serial numbers, is complete, or will be independent of the sampling table. I will in some cases, instead of furnishing the sampling table, specify the exact procedure by which to construct it from a specified table of random numbers.

7. I will furnish instructions for any tabulations that will be necessary to calculate estimates and standard errors or other measures of the statistical significance of the results.

8. The development of the statistical plans may require experimentation and trial, with successive revisions. The client will carry out my instructions for these explorations, and he will stand the expense therefor.

9. I will furnish statistical plans in writing when they are finally fixed, and the client will thereafter make no changes in procedure without further instruction from me so long as my responsibility is in force.

10. I will explain to the client the effect of departures from my instructions. I may require probes of the sampling procedure, and of the coverage, and of the consistency of the tests or interviews, in order to detect and to evaluate any difficulties or departures therefrom. I may also require tests of the computations. The client will carry out these probes according to my instructions, and will furnish to me the results thereof. He will stand the expense therefor.

11. I will furnish at the client's request statistical procedures for him to use as an aid in the supervision of the work, to attain more uniform performance in the testing or in the interviewing and in the coverage than would be possible otherwise.

12. The client will arrange for me to have direct access at any time to the people that carry out the preparation of the sample, the testing or the interviewing, the supervision, and the computations.

13. The client will assume responsibility for those aspects of the problem that are substantive. Specifically, he will:

   a. decide the type of information that the survey or the experiment is to elicit.

   b. prescribe the methods of test, examination, questionnaire, or interview by which to elicit the information.

He will assume responsibility for:

   c. the decision on whether the proposed frame, methods, levels, types, and conditions are sufficiently complete for his purpose.

   d. the decision on the classes and areas of tabulation.

   e. the decision on the precision or protection that is necessary.

   f. the actual work of preparation, training, testing, or interviewing.

   g. the supervision of such work.

   h. the completeness of coverage of sampling units drawn into the sample.

   i. the coding.

   j. the tabulations and the computations.

14. I will explain to the client the meaning of the results of the survey in terms of their statistical significance. However, I will not recommend that he take any specific administrative action or policy. The uses of the data obtained by a survey or experiment are in the end entirely up to the client.

15. My report or testimony will state which aspects of the survey my responsibility included and which it excluded. It will show the estimated standard errors of the results of chief importance, and interpretations of the margins of sampling error therefor, plus useful tests of significance. It will include any meaningful outside comparisons that I made; also interpretation of any formal probe that I prescribed for the detection and measurement of persistent errors that might arise from:

   a. failure to select sampling units according to the procedure prescribed.

   b. failure to reach and to cover sampling units that were designated in the sampling table.

   c. inclusion of sampling units not intended for the sample but covered or partly covered by mistake.

   d. other slips and departures from the procedure prescribed.

   e. errors and difficulties in reporting the results.

   f. wrong information in the documents that form the source of the information.

   g. nonresponse.

My calculations and interpretations will be based on the results that the client furnishes to me. If there was no formal probe, my statement will say so.

16. The client, if he prints or publishes my report, must print it in full, and may not omit any part of it without my consent.

17. The client will not mention my participation in a survey, verbally, or in correspondence, or in print, without my approval. I will furnish any description of the sampling procedure that is to appear in print with my name, and I must see the whole of the accompanying text. The client will pay the cost of my services for this writing.

18. None of the above paragraphs precludes or discourages joint articles with the client or with other participants or with colleagues.

19. I may publish or describe in a professional or scientific meeting the statistical methods that I develop in an engagement. I do not publish actual data or substantive results or other information about the client's business without his permission.

20. I have the privilege of withdrawing at any time from an engagement, and without stating any reason, as I may wish to do if I believe that the client no longer needs my services, or because of dissatisfaction with the questionnaire, or with the method of test, or with the usefulness of the information to be obtained, or with the client's ability to carry out satisfactorily the sampling procedures or any other responsibility that is his. In case of withdrawal, I will send a bill for services rendered.

21. In case of an engagement to develop procedures that the client may take over eventually and follow as regular routine, my judgment will decide when the company is able to follow the procedures without further guidance from me. The company has the right to terminate my services at any time and without stating any reason, but the minimum fee agreed upon at the outset will thereupon be due and payable.

22. Informal consultations and talks that I may carry on with another statistician to exchange experience and advice on sampling plans and methods require no clearance, except by specific restriction.

23. It will be possible and sometimes advantageous to share or to divide the statistical responsibility of a project with another statistician. Nothing in this code precludes a shared or divided responsibility, provided that each person and the client have a definite understanding of what each person is accountable for, jointly or individually. The client will make a separate financial arrangement with me.

24. I will not undertake to do any work that I feel not qualified to do, but will instead, on request, recommend qualified specialists. The client will make his own financial arrangement with the other specialist.

25. The client will assume the financial obligation for my services, and for my traveling expenses.

26. There will be a fee for initial or exploratory consultations, whether they lead to an engagement or not.

27. I will undertake an engagement for a single consultation only if in my judgment there is good promise, on the basis of the proposed agenda, of results that seem to warrant the effort and expense.

28. I have the privilege of turning my practice over to a competent statistician of my choice during any absence that I elect to take. This arrangement will be at my expense. If the client elects to engage some other statistician during my absence, he may do so at his own expense, and subject to my review and satisfaction.

29. I may undertake the review of another statistician's plans, or of a completed survey or experiment, if in my judgment this review might lead to improved statistical practice. I will not make a statement about any plans or about any completed survey or experiment without full opportunity for examination.

QUESTIONS

What are the important considerations as regards mutual responsibilities in sampling surveys of the statistical consultant and the management concerned?

A QUESTIONNAIRE ON CAR SERVICE AND REPAIRS

WHAT MAKE of car do you now own? .... YEAR Model 19................

(If you own more than one, your newest one)

Did you buy it ☐ NEW or ☐ USED?   About how many miles has it been driven?

Date of Purchase .... miles
                   month   year

Please check ☑ the ONE PLACE where you take the above car MOST OFTEN for each of the following:

LUBRICATION
("grease jobs," oil changes, etc.)

☐ Dealer who sold me my car.
☐ Some other new car dealer. *
☐ Garage that does not sell new cars.
☐ Filling station.

MAJOR MECHANICAL REPAIRS
(overhaul or repair of engine, transmission, rear axle, etc.)

☐ Dealer who sold me my car.
☐ Some other new car dealer. *
☐ Garage that does not sell new cars.
☐ Filling station.

MINOR ADJUSTMENTS
(engine tune-up, brake adjustment, other small jobs)

☐ Dealer who sold me my car.
☐ Some other new car dealer. *
☐ Garage that does not sell new cars.
☐ Filling station.

BODY REPAIRS
("bumping," painting, replacing trim, window glass, etc.)

☐ Dealer who sold me my car.
☐ Some other new car dealer. *
☐ Garage that does not sell new cars.
☐ Filling station.

---

* If you checked "Some other new car dealer," what make does he sell? ....

About how long has it been since you took your car in for service to the dealer who sold it to you?

☐ A month or less   ☐ About 3 months   ☐ 6 to 12 months   ☐ Never
☐ About 2 months   ☐ 3 to 6 months   ☐ Over a year

How would YOU rate the service of
THE DEALER WHO SOLD YOU YOUR CAR?

We would appreciate your ratings on the dealer <u>who sold you your car</u>, even if you have not used his service facilities for some time.

Please ✔ check answers

	Good	Fair	Poor
Clean and orderly car receiving department?.........	☐	☐	☐
Do they wait on you promptly?................................	☐	☐	☐
Correct "diagnosis" of trouble?............................. *(good at finding out what's wrong)*	☐	☐	☐
How about quality of work?...................................	☐	☐	☐
Accurate estimates of cost?................................... *—don't usually get an estimate—* ☐	☐	☐	☐
Phoning you about unexpected repairs needed?...	☐	☐	☐
How about attention to minor details?.................	☐	☐	☐
Work completed when promised?.........................	☐	☐	☐
Quick service on lubrication & minor jobs?	☐	☐	☐
Work completed satisfactorily first time? .... *(so you don't have to return for the same job)*	☐	☐	☐
Parts availability in dealer's stock ?........................	☐	☐	☐
Are grease and dirt cleaned off steering wheel, windshield, etc?...	☐	☐	☐
Do they seem to appreciate your patronage?........	☐	☐	☐
Are they courteous and understanding?................	☐	☐	☐

Are the service department prices fair?   ☐ YES   ☐ NO

On the Whole

—how would you rate the service of the dealer who sold you your car?

☐ GOOD   ☐ FAIR   ☐ POOR

Car questionnaire (continued)

If you usually have service performed by the dealer who sold you your car, would you mind checking the reason or reasons?

☐ Convenient location   ☐ Best qualified to service this make
☐ Good quality of service   ☐ Mechanics trained by car manufacturer
☐ Prompt service   ☐ Problems get personal attention
☐ Reasonable charges   ☐ Other reason?..................................

....

After they service your car, do they show any interest, or contact you by mail or phone, to see if you are satisfied with the job they did?

☐ YES   ☐ NO

If you DON'T usually go to the dealer from whom you bought your car, would you mind telling us why?

☐ Moved away from vicinity   ☐ Crowded service department
☐ Disliked quality of service   ☐ Location not convenient
☐ Service charges too high   ☐ Other places open evenings
☐ Disliked their attitude   ☐ Other places give quicker service
     ☐ Some other reason...............................

Has your car needed any service other than lubrication during the past 12 months?

☐ YES   ☐ NO

If "Yes," how do you feel about the amount of service expense on your car during the past 12 months? (except collision work)

☐ Well satisfied; very little service expense.
☐ No serious complaints; ordinary wear and tear expense.
☐ Dissatisfied; excessive amount of service expense.

Can you tell us, without going to any bother, about how much you spent on this car for service during the past 12 months? (Omit lubrication and collision expense) $...

Please check any of the following that have required major repairs or replacement during the past 12 months:

☐ Carburetor   ☐ Muffler, tailpipe   ☐ Body leaks
☐ Electrical System   ☐ Brakes   ☐ Transmission *(Automatic)*
☐ Other engine trouble ☐ Clutch   ☐ Wheel alignment
☐ Radiator   ☐ Transmission *(Standard)* ☐ Collision Repair

     ☐ Other (please specify) ....

....

Car questionnaire (continued)

Suppose you were in the market for a new car right now, would you buy the SAME MAKE you now own?   ☐ Yes ☐ No ☐ Can't say

On the basis of your experience with his service, would you be inclined to buy from the SAME DEALER?   ☐ Yes ☐ No ☐ Can't say

Is there more than one dealer selling your make of car, located near enough so you can choose between one or another dealer for service without going too far out of your way?

☐ Yes ☐ No

Have you had (or do you now have) any service problem with your car that was not handled to your satisfaction by an authorized dealer for your make of car?

☐ Yes, now have
☐ Yes, have had
☐ No

If "Yes", what sort of problem?..

....

....

....

....

Was it necessary for you to communicate with the car Manufacturer (or his representative) about this problem?   ☐ Yes   ☐ No

Was the problem finally handled to your satisfaction?   ☐ Yes   ☐ No

If not, please tell us why...

....

....

....

A Bit Personal —but we would greatly appreciate the following data, which will be used ONLY for statistical cross-analysis:

☐ MAN   ☐ WOMAN   Approx. Age..................

Date this questionnaire filled out...1962

NO SIGNATURE IS NECESSARY, but please tell us your city and state:	Also, if you don't mind, the name of the Dealer from whom you bought your car:
....	....
....	....
....	....
CITY COUNTY STATE	CITY COUNTY STATE

If you own more than one car at present, what make is your other car (or cars)?

MAKE.. Year model............................

★ ★ *Thank You!* ★ ★

Car questionnaire (end)

NATIONAL STATISTICAL SURVEYS

Design of Mail-survey Questionnaire

In making surveys by mail, the design of the questionnaire is of the greatest importance.

Such factors as wording, arrangement, general makeup, length, and so forth, must be reviewed carefully.

A typical questionnaire, as mailed out by National Statistical Surveys of Detroit, Michigan, is shown on pages 101–103.

QUESTIONS

Review the questionnaire from a viewpoint of expected response rate as regards its conduciveness to:

1. Being understood by the randomly sampled addressees.
2. Completeness and accuracy of reply.
3. Motivation to fill out questionnaire.
4. Ease of giving answers.
5. Other factors considered of importance.

Note any improvements that you feel could be made in the questionnaire in regard to the points listed above.

FOOD PACKAGING STUDY

Design of Interview Questionnaire

The questionnaire shown below was developed by a student, as part of a course requirement, in determining food-packaging preferences within the community surrounding his college.

Emphasis in designing the questionnaire was on completeness, ease of answering (check mark only, required), and avoidance of unnecessary length (normal time to fill out questionnaire is 10 minutes).

The questionnaire may serve as a basis for discussing the contents and suggesting improvements. Similar questionnaires on this or other subjects may be found useful for other surveys.

QUESTIONNAIRE

A. Directions: In Part A of the questionnaire, read each question, check your answer, and then go to the next question.

1. Would you change brands of a food product, if a competing brand, of *equal* price and quality compared to your favorite brand, used a new container that you liked?
yes—— no—— undecided——

2. Would you change brands of a food product, if a competing brand of *equal price* but *unknown quality* compared to your favorite brand, used a new container that you liked?
yes—— no—— undecided——

3. Would you change brands of a food product, if a competing brand of *higher price* but *equal quality* compared to your favorite brand, used a new container that you liked?
yes—— no—— undecided——

4. Would you change brands of a food product, if a competing brand of *higher price* but *unknown quality* compared to your favorite brand, used a new container that you liked?
yes—— no—— undecided——

5. Do you feel there is little difference between brands of food products, and hence the container is of particular importance?
yes—— no—— undecided——

6. Do you know the brand of a food product you like, and feel you will continue to use it regardless of how it is packaged?
yes—— no—— undecided——

7. If a new container appeared on the market, would you be more interested in knowing its method of closure rather than the material it is made from?
yes—— no—— undecided——

8. Do you feel, that a new container often does not offer an improvement over the old style, but is the manufacturers way to "stay modern"?
yes—— no—— undecided——

9. Do you feel, that the manufacturer of a food product with the new container is progressive, and hence has a superior product?
yes—— no—— undecided——

10. Do you feel that a new container hides an inferior food product?
yes—— no—— undecided——

11. Would you prefer to use old style food packages at a lower cost?
yes—— no—— undecided——

12. Do you believe that the modernization of a food package results in an increased price?

    yes——   no——   undecided——

B. 1. Which of the following commodities would you prefer to be packaged in plastic, glass, tin, or cardboard?

    Directions: Put a check in the container material column, corresponding to the commodity, that you have selected for an answer.

Item	Plastic	Glass	Tin	Cardboard
Juices	——	——	——	——
Canned fruits and vegetables	——	——	——	——
Frozen fruits and vegetables	——	——	——	——
Canned meat	——	——	——	——
Dry cereals	——	——	——	——
Dairy products	——	——	——	——
Bakery products	——	——	——	——
Waxes and soaps	——	——	——	——
Coffee and tea	——	——	——	——
Other	——	——	——	——

2. Which, of the following characteristics, do you believe a plastic, glass, tin, or cardboard container to have?

    Directions: Put a check in the container material column corresponding to the characteristic that you have selected to be your answer.

Characteristic	Plastic	Glass	Tin	Cardboard
Easy to store	——	——	——	——
Leakproof	——	——	——	——
Visible contents	——	——	——	——
Reusable	——	——	——	——
Nonslip	——	——	——	——
Lightweight	——	——	——	——
Nonbreakable	——	——	——	——
Material does not transfer taste to food	——	——	——	——
Other	——	——	——	——

3. Check the types of container closures that you feel are especially *unsatisfactory*.

Closure Type	Example of Closure
Pry off top	Olive bottle
Screw off top	Baby food jar
Set-n-lid	Cocoa can
Sifter top	Salt container
Spouts	Sugar box

Closure Type	Example of Closure
Pull tab openings	Cake mix box
Stitched tops	Flour bag
Tuck in top	Breakfast cereal box
Key opened metal can	Coffee can
Other	

4. Check the primary reasons why the above indicated container closures were not satisfactory·

Reasons

Contents did not stay fresh.
The contents were not readily accessible.
Closure method was not easy to open.
The closure method resulted in wasted contents.
The closure method could not be readily re-closed.
Other

C. In the final section, I am asking you for ideas. If you have no opinion leave the space blank.

   1. What types of container closures would you like the manufacturers of food product items to make more use of?
   2. Would you like to have packages standardized in shape and size?
   3. Do you like the "family size" package?
   4. Do you have any suggestions as to how to improve packaging for greater consumer convenience?

LAWRENCEVILLE DISTILLING COMPANY (B)

Process Sampling for
Alcohol-yield Evaluation

Al K. Hall, the manager of Lawrenceville Distilling Company, a large industrial alcohol plant, had been puzzling for several months

over the difference in yield on his fermenters. It was particularly
annoying to him that the old fermenter vats in fermenter room A gave
a yield of 6.8 percent alcohol contents, while the new vats in room B
gave a yield of only 6.5 percent.

Alcohol Production

Lawrenceville produced alcohol from corn, ground into meal and
cooked with water. The corn meal is mixed, at 145 degrees F. with
a small amount of malt (sprouted barley), which converts the corn
starch into sugar. The converted mash, after being cooled to fermentation temperature, is pumped into fermenters and yeast is added. Yeast
changes the sugar in the mash to alcohol and carbon-dioxide gas. After
three days' fermentation, the mash has become a "beer" containing
from 6 to 7 percent alcohol. Since water boils at 212 degrees F. and
alcohol boils at 173 degrees F., the alcohol will vaporize at temperatures below the boiling point of water. The vapors containing alcohol
are passed through a condenser (cooler) and are recovered as a liquid.
Milling, conversion, fermentation, and distillation of alcohol is thus
accomplished.

Fermenters

A fermenter holds many thousands of gallons of mash and is usually
2 stories high. On the ground floor, by opening the proper sequence
of valves, beer will flow through the pipes to the master distilling
storage tank. Other valves, when opened, will lead to the sewer, and
are used after caustic cleaning of the empty fermenters. On the second
floor, other pipes bring the mash into the fermenters. The floor is high
enough so that a person, standing near a fermenter, will be able to
bend over it for various operational purposes, including the selection
of samples for yield determination. In general, yield is determined
after 24, 36, and 48 hours each, using a small metal container on a
long chain, which is lowered to the bottom of the fermenter, and then
pulled up with the liquid. Testing is performed in the laboratory,
using spectroscopic and other techniques.

The fermenters in rooms A and B had equal capacity of 30,000
gallons each, but the 30 vats in room A were made of ordinary cast
iron, while the 20 vats in room B were stainless steel. Moreover, in
room B the fermenters had conical bottoms (flat bottoms in A), and
were equipped with a new feature, aeration with compressed air fed
from the bottom of the fermenter.

Both rooms fed into the same distillation storage tank.

Further Yield Losses

As the months dragged by and no one seemed able to come up with a satisfactory solution, it was rumored throughout the plant that the person who could demonstrate the reason for the difference in yield between the two types of fermenters would be likely to be handsomely rewarded with advancement, since obviously such a person would have unlocked some of the "unknowns" still prevailing in fermentation processes. One of the chief theories was that the stainless-steel vats did not interact with the mash, while the cast-iron vats did, and that this interaction enhanced alcohol production by the yeast cells.

Further Checks

The difference in yield between the two fermenter rooms had been pointed out originally, by Fred Drinkwater, who was working in the testing laboratory and was maintaining control charts. Fred thought that possibly, a statistically designed multifactor experiment would be desirable to investigate the yield factors. He sought and obtained permission to attend a two-week course on statistical methods for the chemical industry, given in the Midwest and sponsored by the American Society for Quality Control and the American Chemical Society.

When Fred returned, he suggested that prior to a large-scale experiment, some other simple factors be checked. One of these factors turned out to be the answer to the yield-difference problem.

QUESTIONS

What would be some of the simple factors that should be checked?

THE GOLDEN NUGGET, LAS VEGAS, NEVADA[1]

Sampling Control in Casino Operations

The Golden Nugget, located in fashionable Las Vegas, Nevada, has a weekly turnover of several million dollars at its gambling tables,

---

[1] Case data based on a paper presented in 1961 by Charles Hirsch, controller, The Golden Nugget, at the annual meeting of the American Society for Quality Control, in Philadelphia.

retaining on the average a small fraction as the house percentage, known in the trade as "house mark-up."

The house uses some 4000 pairs of dice weekly. Lots are purchased in quantities of 10,000 from two sources of supply. The dice are subjected to a very careful check, using visual inspection, micrometers, weighing scales, and an electronic evenness tester. Because of the considerable testing and inspection expense involved, it was suggested that a procedure of sampling inspection be used. Development of such a sampling procedure would involve the establishment of an allowable percent defective, adoption of a sampling plan, and maintenance of quality history records by suppliers.

QUESTIONS

Assuming that the acceptable quality level is one-half of one percent and that a sequential sampling procedure is to be used, prepare for management your recommendations as concerns:
1. Specific sampling plan and the corresponding sampling risks.
2. Quality history record form.
3. Advantages of this sampling over present methods.

VIRGINIA ELECTRIC AND POWER COMPANY

Sampling of Watt-hour Meters

The Virginia Electric and Power Company developed a sampling program, for use in determining an effective maintenance program for the care of the great number of single-phase meters in service. As part of the program, a brochure was issued to the personnel of the company explaining the value of the statistically designed sampling program. Following are the essential portions of this brochure.

Purpose

The purposes of this outline are to present a proposed plan for improving and assuring sustained accuracy of single phase watt-hour meters in service; and to demonstrate that the customer and the Company will benefit by the substitution of a selective test plan for the present system of periodic meter testing.

Regulatory commissions and utilities have long recognized the need for meter testing to maintain overall meter accuracy as a means of insuring correct customer billing. In former years, it was necessary that meters be tested at relatively frequent intervals, therefore, maintenance of meter accuracy was more of a problem than now. The development of overload and temperature compensating devices, new magnetic steels and other improvements have been reflected in the periodic test system and, as a result, test periods for single phase watt-hour meters have been increased from two or three years to as much as 20 years in some jurisdictions. Under present regulations, the test program of the Virginia Electric and Power Company calls for each meter to be tested once every eight years. The Virginia Commission has established ± 2% as the limits of acceptable accuracy.

Advantages of Selective Meter Testing

1. By testing selectively, time spent on meter testing may be utilized more efficiently. A modern sampling procedure will point out the types of meters that may be in need of recalibration and, therefore, time is not wasted in testing meter groups where the need for recalibration is not indicated.

2. Through the use of modern sampling procedures, data of measured reliability with respect to the performance of various meter types, and service under varying conditions of use, may be obtained. This is not possible under the periodic testing system now in use.

3. Meter types that may not retain accuracy for extended periods of time will be disclosed by the sampling procedure and will be tested more frequently than every eighth year and will be subject to earlier retirement.

4. Selective Testing is compatible with what is believed to be the ultimate solution of the meter accuracy problem; development of a low cost single-phase watt-hour meter which will maintain desired accuracy for its life of 15 to 20 years and then be replaced by a new meter.

Present Periodic Test Program

Under the existing periodic test program, the Company tests something over 100,000 meters each year and, with the anticipated growth in customers, this number will increase substantially. Experience over a number of years indicates that more than 98 percent of all single-phase watt-hour meters in service are recording within the established limits of accuracy. Thus, in order to locate 2 meters that are in need of recalibration, it is necessary to test 100 meters. This is an inefficient, unwieldy and time-consuming operation.

Selective Testing Procedure

The fundamentals of the selective plan are these:

1. Devise a means for determining the types or groups of meters that require recalibration.
2. Concentrate meter-test activity on such meters.
3. Retire as rapidly as possible meters that will not hold calibration.

The basic problem of any test program is to determine which meters are in need of recalibration. In view of major meter-design improvements made around 1928, 1934, and 1939, it is logical to expect that meters built before 1928 will not maintain their accuracies as well as late models. On this basis, a 10 percent sample of meters tested during 1955 was drawn in three Company districts; each of these three samples supports the belief that the older meters would be those most often found outside of the accuracy limits. Under the 8-year test schedule, in the Richmond District, 5.24 percent of the meters manufactured between 1910 and 1928 were found to be more than 2 percent fast, whereas all of the meters manufactured between 1939 and 1955 were well within the established limits of accuracy. Similar conditions of relative accuracy by age groups were found in the other two districts. These data demonstrate that the age of meters is a definite indication of the proportion of meters which may be expected to require recalibration.

Modern sampling methods currently in use in market research, industrial quality control, and in the gathering of business statistics may be applied to determine the meter types that may need calibration. The manufacturer's type and serial number will indicate which meters contain the modern improvements and may be used as a key for classification purposes.

After selection, testing, and analysis of a proper sample group of meters per year, each district will concentrate test activities on those types of meters which the sample indicates are in need of attention. Little or no testing would be required within the groups which, according to the sample, are within the established limits of accuracy, since data now available indicate that the newer types of meters may be expected to remain within the accepted limits of accuracy until scheduled retirement.

The drawing of a new sample each year will result in an annual appraisal of the relative performance of meters by types in service and of changes in overall accuracy. Under the present program, no reliable measure of overall accuracy is possible because of the method used in selecting meters for test. Under periodic testing, activity in one year may be concentrated on new meters, while in other years older types will predominate, thus giving false indications of overall accuracies from year to year.

For analytical purposes the sample may be broken down into subgroups by areas or by certain characteristics that affect performance. Such analysis will include a study of performance in areas particularly subject to lightning damage or exposure to corrosive atmospheric conditions.

In future years, the types of meters and adverse locations now affecting meters may no longer be important, but new problems may develop. Such changes will be revealed as they occur by analysis of the annual sample, thus directing concentrated test activity to areas of greatest need.

The selective testing procedure here proposed is intended to apply only to single-phase watt-hour meters used without auxiliary equipment. All polyphase meters, and single-phase meters with instrument transformers, will be tested at regular periodic intervals in accordance with an attached proposed filing.

Under the proposed program, at any time, any meter that is suspected of being inaccurate will be tested. Meters that become inoperative either through mechanical or electrical damage will be located, repaired, or replaced under existing procedures.

QUESTIONS

Develop recommended sampling procedures and detailed single- and sequential-sampling plans for use with the proposed meter-sampling program.

JUMBO COLA COMPANY (C)

Work Sampling Study of Plant Labor Utilization

The head-office bottling plant of the Jumbo Cola Company desired to study the utilization of labor in the various productive departments, from receiving and mixing through bottling and loading-shipping. Approximately 60 employees were working in the plant.

In order to obtain a quick overall evaluation, a work-sampling study was performed, consisting of 10 complete walk-throughs per day. The observer had to select the time of each walk-through at random and, in addition, followed a random path, making sure nevertheless to cover all productive departments. For each employee, a note was made as to whether, at the particular moment of observation, he was actively engaged, inactive (in the working area, but waiting), idle, or absent from the department. The results are shown in Table VI-1.

TABLE VI-1. UTILIZATION OF PLANT LABOR*

Observation Date	Actively Engaged		Inactive (in Work Area, Waiting)		Idle		Absent from Department	
	No.	Percent	No.	Percent	No.	Percent	No.	Percent
Nov. 13	39	66.1	6	10.2	10	16.9	4	6.8
14	37	62.7	5	8.5	4	6.8	15	25.0
15	39	61.8	6	9.6	2	3.2	16	25.4
17	34	54.0	9	14.3	4	6.3	16	25.4
Average	37.2	60.7	6.5	10.5	5.0	8.2	12.7	20.6

* Data based on 10 plant-wide observations per day, using work-sampling technique.

QUESTIONS

What conclusions would you draw from the work-sampling data obtained? Where applicable, support your conclusions with statistical confidence limits or other pertinent statistical criteria.

LUKENS STEEL COMPANY

Audit of Incentive Standards, Using Sampling and Evaluation of Paired Differences

One of the major problems in all wage-incentive plans is the maintenance of accurate standards over a period of years.

At Lukens, the planned program for maintaining the equity of production standards comprises several different controls, the most effective of which is a periodic audit of all the company's premium-pay plans, now numbering over 100. Naturally, with such a volume of incentive plans to be covered, it is difficult to complete the audit cycle as often as one would like. An approximate two-year frequency of review is the goal for this phase. To keep these audits unbiased, and likewise to maintain a consistent viewpoint of standard throughout the plant, this function is handled by a small group reporting directly to the manager of industrial engineering.

As the original standards have been set by time study, this review, or audit, consequently, is made using the same procedure. Customarily, these audits have been almost as comprehensive and thorough as was the process of developing the standards initially. As such a procedure takes considerable time, one is confronted with the problem of keeping up with a constantly broadening schedule. With the problem in mind of how best to accelerate the auditing procedure, Lukens began to investigate statistical techniques. In order to prove effective, these statistical techniques would have to accomplish two objectives:

1. They would have to reduce the overall time spent in making the audit.
2. They would have to provide a degree of reliability comparable to the more comprehensive procedures.

The Statistical Problem

The foregoing represents the auditing problem, that is, how could audit time per investigation be reduced (so as to permit faster coverage) while maintaining sufficient reliability in the results of the method employed? The statistical problem is one of hypothesis testing, based on sampling theory, and contains the following elements:

1. An underlying "true" situation exists.
   a. The standard validly covers present performance.
   b. The standard does not validly cover present performance.
2. Using sampling, a certain number of observations will be taken that will be used to test the above hypotheses.
3. The auditor can make two errors (in statistical language errors of the first and second kind) in testing hypotheses with sample data.
   a. He can say that a difference exists between prevailing standard and true current operation, when, in fact, no difference does exist (error of the first kind, or alpha).
   b. He can say that a difference does not exist between prevailing standard true current operation, when, in fact, a difference does exist (error of the second kind, or beta).

The Setting of the Problem

Most time-study standards are set up in relation to certain characteristics of the product, such as weight, diameter, gauge, and surface area. Inasmuch as the nature of Lukens' business is largely job-shop, the tables were designed to cover as wide a variation in product mix as practicable. Table VI-2 is a typical example from a standards bulletin.

TABLE VI-2.   INCENTIVE STANDARDS FOR BACKING-PLATE OPERATION

Standard Time to Flatten Carbon Steel Plates on No. 3 Press

Plate Area (Sq. In.)	Standard (Hr./Piece)	Plate Area (Sq. In.)	Standard (Hr./Piece)
1000	0.14	6000	0.24
1500	.15	6500	.25
2000	.16	7000	.26
2500	.17	7500	.27
3000	.18	8000	.28
3500	.19	8500	.29
4000	.20	9000	.30
4500	.21	9500	.31
5000	.22	10,000	.32
5500	.23		

As can be seen in the table, the relationship is linear within the range covered and amounts to a 0.02 standard hour increase per 1000 square-inch increase in plate area.

"Proving out" the accuracy of tables such as these can be a perplexing problem. The auditor can find, for example, that the lower section of the table is loose and the upper section tight, so that, over-all, the 2 may tend to balance out. Although situations such as these can arise, the audit group must always weigh the cost needed for greater accuracy against the payoff derived from the finer degree of accuracy. From the standpoint of departmental policy, "accuracy" pertains to the average accuracy of the total table and not to that of each individual standard.

The Method of Paired Differences

For the tests to be discussed it may be assumed that the sample observations (time studies) are taken at random and are representative of the normal universe under study. Although these conditions are often difficult to meet in practice, preliminary checks indicated that these requirements could be approximated. The procedure thus is as follows:

1. The standards auditor proceeds to take a representative sample of the work flow covered by the standards under study. This sample is checked by product mix characteristics prior to audit so as to achieve the desired representativeness.

2. The time-study data is then converted into standard hours per piece.
3. Paired differences of sample times minus the present standard times are computed.
4. These differences are subjected to a statistical "t" test.
5. Based upon the results of this test, the auditor decides within certain error risks to:
   a. Accept hypothesis that standard is adequate coverage of present performance.
   b. Reject hypothesis that standard is adequate coverage of present performance.
   c. Take more observations until a or b is finally reached.
6. When conclusions have been reached from these tests, the results and accompanying recommendations are submitted in writing to the operating superintendent and to the zone industrial engineer responsible for the particular incentive plan. If corrections are necessary, the zone engineer then has sufficient additional studies taken to revise the production standards.

Referring again to Table VI-2, the standards auditor took current studies on the backing plate operation and obtained the data shown in Table VI-3.

TABLE VI-3. WORK SAMPLING RESULTS ON BACKING-PLATE OPERATION

Observed Times to Flatten Carbon Steel Backing Plates on No. 3 Press

Plate Area Sq. In.	Hours per Piece
1500	0.16; 0.13
2000	.14; .16
3500	.17; .18; 0.19
6000	.21; .22; .25
8500	.27; .31
9000	.27; .29
10,000	.33

QUESTIONS

Does the sample evidence indicate that the present standard validly covers true current operations?

CAKE-FROSTING SURVEY [2]

Replicated Sampling in Consumer Research

The management of a large food manufacturing firm desired to investigate the marketing potentials of a new cake-frosting mix. Based on work with a consultant in statistical surveys, a small nationwide survey, comprising 1200 interviews with female homemakers, was conducted.

Within 400 segments of area, among the four census regions of the U. S. selected for the sample, there were 1961 dwelling units included in the survey. A total of 791 out of the 1961 female homemakers, or 40 percent answered "yes" to the first part of the question: "Do you make your own cake frosting at home, or do you prefer to buy a mix?" The 60 percent thus represented instances of a "no" answer, dwelling units with no female homemakers, and some nonresponses.

Replication and Control

The sampling was so arranged that there was complete replication. This involved splitting each sample in two, with each of the 400 segments of area being separately by two interviewers. Thus, each sample consisted of two subsamples. The variance *between individual interviewers*, evaluated from the replicated samples, proved to be generally within normally expected ranges, and there were no significant differences between *individual sets of subsamples*. Had there been significant differences, then this would have indicated probable operational errors in need of investigation and correction. It should be noted that, although each segment of area was worked by two separately operating interviewers, provision was made that no dwelling unit was interviewed twice.

A statistical control audit, by means of re-examining a small randomly chosen portion of the work from the table of random numbers used, on through the field work, and into the coding and punching of the data, did not uncover any significant effects, such as might have been caused by any persistent omissions or any overcount or undercount of any characteristic. The purpose of such statistical control is generally not to make any corrections of the main sample, but to provide information of value in interpreting the results.

---

[2] Case prepared from material due to Dr. W. Edwards Deming, Consultant in Statistical Surveys, Washington, D. C.

Probability Sampling

The survey was carried out within accepted principles of valid probability sampling, involving the following activities:

1. Statement and formulation of the problem in concise meaningful terms (the statistical model), so that the study will yield useful information within allowable costs.

2. Specification and preparation of a suitable frame for sampling, represented by lists of areas and dwelling units.

3. Specification of the procedure for the selection of a suitable number of sampling units for investigation using random numbers with stratification. The sampling procedures contained rules for recalls on people not at home at the initial call, or on subsequent attempts.

4. The formula or procedure for formation of estimates, based on the selections made under (3) above, so as to maximize the amount of information per unit cost, within the practical limitations of the survey.

5. The formula or procedure for formation of standard errors, to measure the margin of uncertainty that arises from variability in the material and from variable performance of the investigators, coders, punchers, and other workers.

6. Design of records and statistical controls to assist supervision by detection of nonuniform performance in the field and in the office and to detect and evaluate nonsampling errors, especially persistent operational blemishes of investigators, coders, punchers, and other workers.

7. Interpretation of the results and their presentation for the non-statistician.

8. Analysis of the statistical controls, variance components, and costs to improve the sample-design for subsequent studies, achieve better allocation of resources, and enhance the efficiency of office work, selection of investigators, and training and supervision.

Probability sampling is thus not merely selecting units for test, but rather continually applying of the theory of probability to effect improvement of operations in field and office and to achieve the best use of resources, directed toward the central aim of the research investigation or survey.

Some people would call this activity operational research or systems analysis or something of the sort, but to a statistician, what is outlined above as probability sampling is only good statistical practice, and it has been his activity for many years.

Probability sampling does not generate problems nor take action on them. Probability sampling is the application of statistical techniques in ways indicated above to assist design, production, marketing, distribution, and other human activities.

Division of Responsibility

In conducting a consumer-research survey, such as discussed in this case, problems arise as to the division of responsibility among management, the statistician, and the specialist or expert in the subject matter under investigation. This problem may be resolved best when the basic elements of work are considered:

1. *The universe.* The universe in a statistical study is all the people or firms or material, conditions, concentrations, models, or levels that one wishes to draw conclusions about or to take action on, whether accessible or not. The universe will be clear from a careful statement of the problem. In the present case, it is all female homemakers. In other cases it may be all the firms that make or buy a certain product, all school children, or all the material or piece-parts in a lot, or certain records within a company. In each instance the problem of a proper definition of the universe is nonstatistical: it has its origin in knowledge of the subject-matter, through which one senses the existence of a problem and has ideas on what to do about it. The universe in any problem would be the same whether one planned to use sampling or not.

2. *The frame.* The frame is part of the statistical model, representing a set of physical materials called sampling units, such as are represented in census data, maps, lists, directories and records, that enable one to take hold of parts of the universe, piece-by-piece. To be useful, the frame must include enough area and a sufficiently wide range of conditions, since no sampling plan can overcome deficiencies in the frame. Statistical inference carried on the basis of the sampling data covers only the given frame and the conditions subjected to the sampling procedure. Generalizations to other cities, climates, conditions, and levels not covered by the frame nor subjected to the sampling procedure require subjective judgment, not statistical theory. Thus, if a product is tested by a survey carried out, however expertly, in Chicago, no statistical theory will enable one to generalize the results to include Denver. Such nonstatistical generalization may be made only by subjective judgment.

3. *Standard error.* A proper multiple of the standard error evaluates

the possible magnitude of uncertainty in the results that one could reasonably ascribe to sampling and to variable operational errors.

4. *Statistical control.* The purpose of the statistical control, or audit, is to evaluate any persistent operational errors that occurred, as was previously discussed. In probability sampling carefully carried out, no doubt is left about the uncertainties that could arise from repeated selection and processing, nor from operational blemishes.

It is apparent that deficiencies built into a study through incompleteness in the frame, through faulty test procedures, or faulty techniques of questioning or of interviewing are not errors of sampling, nor in fact of a complete coverage either. Built-in deficiencies are still there, whether it is sample or complete coverage. Built-in deficiencies can be discovered and reduced only through improved knowledge of the subject matter, possibly aided by actual comparisons of two or more methods of test.

Logical division of responsibility now becomes clear. The content of the questionnaire, the method of tests or of interviewing, the coding, and finally, after the study is completed, the generalization of the results beyond the frame and beyond conditions not subjected to the sampling procedure, are the responsibilities of experts in the subject matter under investigation. In contrast, the probability design of a sample or of an experiment and the objective inferences that are possible with the theory of probability are the responsibility of the statistician. Action, if any, with or without the results of a study, belongs to management.

Results of Survey

A summary of the survey, for the four Census regions, Northeast, North Central, South and West, is given in Exhibit 1.

From the data, an estimate was made of the total number of dwelling units in the United States, which fell short by only two percent or about one standard error of the Census figure. This small difference seemed to indicate that persistent undercoverages of assigned segments of area, if there were any, were probably of small magnitude.

Evaluation of Results

The following are some of the analyses that may now be performed in evaluating the data in Table VI-4.

1. Variance in number of "yes" answers:
   a. between subsamples,

TABLE VI-4. RESULTS OF CAKE-FROSTING SURVEY

	Northeast		North Central		South		West		U.S.
	Metro-politan	Nonmetro-politan	Metro-politan	Nonmetro-politan	Metro-politan	Nonmetro-politan	Metro-politan	Nonmetro-politan	Total (1)-(8)
	(1)	(2)	(3)	(4)	(5)	(6)	(7)	(8)	(9)
a. No. answering "Yes"									
a_1 Subsample 1	98	35	100	33	40	47	38	33	424
a_2 Subsample 2	79	17	69	38	38	52	45	29	357
Total	177	52	169	71	78	99	83	62	791
b. No. of dwelling units selected									
b_1 Subsample 1	213	64	203	94	123	174	87	62	1020
b_2 Subsample 2	176	55	162	128	110	165	89	56	941
Total	389	119	365	222	233	339	176	118	1961
c. "Yes" answers obtained, % (100 a/b)	45.5	43.7	46.3	32.0	33.5	29.2	47.2	52.5	40.0

Source: Data provided through the courtesy of Dr. W. Edwards Deming, Consultant in Statistical Surveys, Washington, D. C.

    b. between metropolitan and nonmetropolitan areas,

    c. among regions.

2. Significance of differences in proportion of "yes" answers, between subsamples, between metropolitan and nonmetropolitan areas and among regions.

3. Significance of difference of variance in "yes" answers between the two subsamples.

4. Analyses similar to (1)-(3) for number of dwelling units.

5. Standard error, σ_p, of the final estimate of the proportion, ρ, of 0.40 "yes" answers for the United States, using the formula:

$\hat{\sigma}_p = S/b$, where

$S^2 = \Sigma\,[(a_1 - a_2) - p\,(b_1 - b_2)]^2$

with a and b taken from Table VI-4.

6. Upper and lower 1-percent fiducial limits, using 7 degrees of freedom. (The degrees of freedom figure actually is somewhat less than 8, because of unequal variances contributed by the different geographic regions. See F. E. Satterthwaite, *Biometrics*, Vol. 2, pp. 110-114, 1946.)

From this information, especially as regards the standard error and fiducial limits, the findings can be presented to provide useful information to management in making decisions and plans concerning the marketing of the new cake-frosting mix.

QUESTIONS

Report your findings to management.

SOCIETY OF BUSINESS ADVISORY PROFESSIONS

Standards of Probability Sampling

The Society of Business Advisory Professions, Inc., in cooperation with the Graduate School of Business Administration of New York University, is an organization of distinguished professional persons who are interested in the mutual interchange of ideas and opinions on problems of contemporary significance. Through the media of conferences, informal seminars, special monographs, and the official publication of the Society, "Current Business Studies," economists, lawyers, accountants, trade association executives, management consultants,

and financial consultants obtain the benefit of the others' views concerning problems of common interest. The opportunity for discussion
with outstanding professional advisors to business, in an atmosphere
of personal friendship, is considered to be one of the main advantages
of membership in the Society.

The use of economic data as evidence in many kinds of legal pro-
ceedings that originate in the business field has increased greatly in
recent times. A series of conferences to study some of the problems
of handling such data was begun by the Society of Business Advisory
Professions in 1954.

A meeting dealing with the role of sampling data aroused wide-
spread interest. The speakers underlined the lack of criteria to
govern the presentation and interpretation sample-survey data as
legal evidence. They also stressed the immediate need for some competent body to undertake the task of framing a statement of sampling
standards acceptable to both lawyers and judges.

Out of this background came the recommendation that the president of the Society appoint a committee—to consist of persons representing the various professional interests among the membership and
who were especially well qualified for the task by training and experience—that would be authorized to formulate and publish a statement of suitable standards of sampling for legal evidence. The committee completed its work, and the product of its efforts is presented
in the pages that follow.

STANDARDS OF PROBABILITY SAMPLING
FOR LEGAL EVIDENCE

Admissibility of Data from Probability Samples

Scope and purpose. The standards that follow are intended to govern in
legal evidence the presentation and interpretation of data obtained by
probability sampling as defined later. Other forms of sampling or partial
surveys or enumerations are not included in this document. The use of data
produced by one of these other methods should be justified by criteria
appropriate to its nature and to the circumstances.

These standards establish specifications for sampling, which if certified
as followed, and provided the standard error of the sample-result is small
enough to be innocuous, should establish the acceptance of the numerical
result of a sample as legal evidence, on the same status as the result of an
equal complete coverage of all the units in the same frame (q.v.) whence
the sample came, without the requirement of a dissertation on the theory,
techniques, meaning, and reliability of sampling.

An equal complete coverage is a coverage of all the sampling units (a 100 percent sample) in the same frame as was used for the sample, under the stipulation that the complete coverage was carried out with the same procedure as was used for the sample for eliciting the information, with the same thoroughness, and over about the same period of time.

Disclaimers. These standards do not specify what kinds of information might be useful or admissible in any case; nor do they deal with the methods, definitions, and techniques by which such information is to be elicited from people, business establishments, or records; nor do they describe methods for testing industrial product; nor do they lay down the criteria for making an audit of a financial statement by professional accountants. They offer no criteria by which to evaluate the usefulness or the scientific value of any data. They offer no criteria by which one decides whether a given frame will give adequate coverage of the universe that one desires to study. Judgment on these matters must come from experts in the subject-matter and from experts in the techniques of interviewing and testing. Statistical theory cannot accomplish this judgment, although experiments designed with the aid of statistical theory will estimate the numerical differences between the results to be expected from different methods, definitions, and techniques, or between two sets of inspectors or interviewers. Such questions are the same whether the survey is to be conducted by a sample, large or small, or by a complete coverage.

Basis of admissibility. If a study would be admissible evidence as a complete coverage of a certain frame, then it will also be admissible if it is carried out as a probability sample of that frame.

a. An exception occurs if the precision of the sample is too low for the purpose, or if flaws in execution render the results questionable.

b. In most respects, the preparation, execution, interpretation, and use of survey-data are the same whether the survey be a complete coverage or a probability sample. The problems created by a gap between the frame and the universe, by the questionnaire, by the procedure of testing, or interviewing, or by the coding, the interpretation, and the judgment of the expert on the usefulness or the propriety of the data for the problem at hand, are the same for a sample and for an equal complete coverage.

c. The chief difference is that data from a sample possess error from the use of sampling in place of a complete coverage of the same frame, but the margin of error with its associated probability is calculable and is known objectively; it is not a matter of judgment nor of expert opinion, but is a mathematical consequence.

d. Another difference is that the quality of the testing, interviewing, supervision, coding in a sample-survey can be superior to the quality of a complete coverage, and the accuracy of the sample-survey can thus be the greater, provided one takes advantage of the smaller size of the job.

Form of the results. The result of a sample will be in the form of a numerical upper (lower) limit that one may accept, with a stated probability, as above (below) the result that would have come from an equal complete coverage of the same frame. The result of a sample is sometimes in the form of both an upper limit and a lower limit that one may accept, with a stated probability, as including the result of the equal complete coverage.

Definition. Probability sampling is a procedure by which one obtains a result from a selected portion of a total number of establishments, accounts, or other items, that will be the same, within calculable limits of uncertainty, as the result that would have come from an equal complete coverage, namely, an examination of all the establishments, accounts, or other items in the frame with the same definitions and care as were expended on the sample. The special feature of probability sampling is that it permits use of the theory of probability for the computation, from the sample itself, of the margin of error and the probability associated therewith that has been introduced by the use of a sample in place of an equal complete coverage.

The frame. The objective inferences in regard to the precision of a sample refer to the frame, but owing to gaps between the frame and the universe, wherein the frame fails to cover the universe, these inferences do not necessarily apply to the universe. To be acceptable, the frame whence a sample will be drawn, together with the accompanying procedures for covering any sampling unit once drawn from the frame, must yield, when the sample is increased to 100% of the sampling units of the frame, a satisfactory coverage of the universe that one desires to study.

a. The frame is composed of sampling units, the totality of which, if covered by the survey, would constitute a 100% sample. The frame is often in the form of a list of sampling units. Each sampling unit in the frame may contain people, firms, product, or records, that are capable of furnishing the information that is desired in the study.

b. A frame is a means of access to the universe. Without a frame there can be neither a complete coverage nor a probability sample.

c. Sampling can not overcome the fundamental defects of a frame, nor of any procedure for using it. Any hazard that arises from incompleteness in the frame or from any proposed method of covering a sampling unit will persist undiminished, no matter how big the sample, even if it includes all the sampling units of the frame. If this hazard is great enough, the frame may not be suitable for either a complete coverage or a sample.

THE PRECISION OF A RESULT

The index of precision. The index of the precision of any estimate is its standard error, or an objective estimate thereof. The margin of difference between an estimate made from a sample, and the result that would have been obtained from an equal complete coverage, is usually expressed as an appropriate multiple of the estimate of the standard error, for a specified probability or risk.

The limits of sampling error. The maximum uncertainty in any estimate that is made from a sample used in place of an equal complete coverage of the same frame may be placed at 3 times the standard error of the estimate.

a. The actual difference between (a) the estimate produced by the sample and (b) the result of a complete coverage carried out under the same conditions, is usually much less, and may be in either direction. Only about 1 estimate in 40 will fall below 2 standard errors from the result of a complete coverage, and only about 1 in 40 will fall above 2 standard errors.

b. If the sample is very small (below 25 independent sampling units), or if the distribution in the frame is highly skewed, the calculations of the margin of error, also its interpretation, should be carried out with the aid of the theory of probability, with regard for the distributions involved.

c. This interpretation of a statistical calculation such as the standard error is not a matter of opinion, nor of judgment, but is a mathematical consequence.

d. Every characteristic estimated from a sample has its own standard error, and any standard error depends upon the sample-design that was used.

Size of sample. The size of a sample is not sufficient information by which to calculate the standard error of a result. The procedure for the selection of the sampling units, and for the calculation of the estimates, are equally as important as the size.

The size of a sample is not by itself a criterion of its precision, nor of its accuracy, nor of its usefulness.

Information provided by the standard error. Once a sampling survey is completed, and an estimate is obtained therefrom, the standard error of this estimate, or the margin of error and its associated probability, calculated (a) by the proper statistical theory from the results of the sample, and (b) under the necessary conditions for validity (use of random numbers, adherence to the prescribed sampling procedure) conveys all the information that there is in regard to the precision of the estimate in question.

Information not provided by the standard error. A standard error, or a margin of error, does not however convey all the information that there is in regard to blemishes in the execution of the sampling procedure.

Details concerning the sampling procedure, such as the modes of stratification, and the statistician's reasons for his choices of plan and for the size and description of the sampling units, convey no new information about the precision of an estimate, once the numerical value of its standard error is known. The only reason for including such information in the testimony is to permit probe of the execution of the sampling procedure.

RANDOMNESS

Random numbers. A system of selection that depends on the use in a standard manner of an acceptable table of random numbers shall be accepted as random.

Other devices. Mechanical devices that depend on physical mixing or shuffling are hazardous and are not acceptable as random without proof, which will require the aid of statistical techniques. The words "thorough mixing," for example, have no standard meaning.

Any method of selection that merely removes the choice of the sampling units from the judgment of the interviewer, without giving definite relative probabilities to each unit, does not constitute a random selection, and does not produce a probability sample.

THE STATISTICIAN'S TESTIMONY

The statistician's testimony should include a statement of his responsibility in the engagement: what it included, and what it did not include.

The sample-design and the instructions for carrying it out should be written, and should be available, to be made part of the evidence, if a probe of the execution of the sample-design is required. The written sample-design and instructions should include:

a. The frame or frames. If a frame is supplanted in some of the steps by rules for the allotment of serial numbers to certain units, these rules should be written, in order that the selection and identification of these units may be retraced. (Files or other material that are necessarily in constant use may change from day to day and render retracing difficult or impossible.)

b. The method of defining and of covering a sampling unit.

c. The procedure for drawing the sampling units. The rules for the identification and for the coverage of a sampling unit.

d. The source of the random numbers and the method of using them.

e. The formula or the procedure for forming the estimates.

f. The formula or the procedure for calculating the standard errors of these estimates (by which to compute the margin of error for any estimate).

The interviewers' or the inspectors' original forms, and the cards or worksheets derived therefrom, should be filed so that it is possible to retrace the transfer of information from the original entries through the tabulations, and to repeat any calculations for the estimates or for their standard errors.

There should be evidence to show whether the serialization of the sampling units in the frame was carried out independently of the drawing of the random numbers. This condition is satisfied if the frame and the serialization of the sampling units therein were completed prior to the drawing of the random numbers. If the random numbers were drawn by the survey organization, the starting point in the table and the method for abstracting the random numbers therefrom should be specified by the consulting statistician so that the selections may be retraced.

The statistician's testimony should include a statement of steps that he took to ensure understanding of the procedure, and tests of compliance. It should describe:

a. The steps that he took to measure—

   i. the proportion of failures to cover the sampling units properly and in the manner prescribed;

   ii. the proportion of sampling units not intended for the sample but covered or partly covered by mistake;

   iii. the errors and difficulties in reporting;

   iv. nonresponse;

   v. slips and blemishes in the execution of the sampling procedure;

   vi. surprises in the material sampled, and their possible effects on the results and on their standard errors (e.g., the discovery of large accounts in the sample, when none was suspected when the sampling plan was drawn up).

b. Their possible effects on conclusions drawn or to be drawn from the data.

QUESTIONS

1. How is the validity and efficiency of a sampling design attained?
2. What does a small standard error mean?
3. Is a sampling result of value if it has a large sampling error?
4. To what extent will the number of sampling units in the frame affect the precision of a sample?

Chapter VII

TIME SERIES AND FORECASTING

LYNCHBURG FOUNDRY COMPANY [1]

Time Series and Frequency-distribution Analysis of Supplies Inventories

Mr. E. F. Pierce, Manager of the Methods Department of the Lynchburg Foundry Company, was checking the records of cut-off wheels used by the company in its ductile iron work. Increased ductile iron production in the past 12 months had required a corresponding increase in the use of cut-off wheels and a more than proportional increase in the average level of stocks of wheels. Since the trend in ductile iron was expected to continue, Mr. Pierce was interested in establishing a policy that would control the chance of being out of wheels when they were needed but that at the same time would not require an excessive amount of inventory of wheels to be carried.

The Lynchburg Foundry Company had two plants in south-western Virginia, and it employed over 1000 workers. The company was founded in the 1890's to produce agricultural implements and parts for agricultural machinery. It expanded rapidly in this field and in 1906 added equipment to produce cast-iron pipe. Over the next fifty years, the company diversified further into military and industrial markets. The company management placed great emphasis on research and development, and this policy, through the years, resulted in many advantages for the company in the fields of metallurgy and foundry practice.

[1] Adapted with permission of authors, publisher, and Lynchburg Foundry Company from R. W. Cabell and A. Phillips, *Problems in Basic Operations Research for Management* (New York: John Wiley & Sons, 1961), p. 36-41.

Until 1949 most of the output of the foundry in Lynchburg had been gray iron castings. In that year, however, the company was licensed by the International Nickel Company to produce ductile iron, and an experimental program was undertaken which would lead eventually to large-scale production of ductile iron. Ductile iron is produced by chemically treating iron in its molten state to give it greater strength and ductility. The main advantage of ductile iron over gray iron is that ductile iron is not as brittle as gray iron and, hence, cannot be broken as easily as gray iron. Most of the production processes for the two types of iron are similar; however, some changes are necessary in the steps following the casting of the ductile iron.

In producing a casting, provisions must be made for the introduction of molten metal into the mold and for flow of molten metal into spaces created by the cooling, contracting metal in the castings. To meet these requirements, channels and spaces are provided in the mold to supply molten metal to the casting itself. After cooling, the metal in these spaces remains attached to the casting and must be removed. The complete casting is removed from the mold, and these "gates and risers" (as they are called) usually are knocked off the gray iron castings by a blow of some kind, and the remaining small protrusions are removed with a grinding wheel. For ductile iron, however, because of the quality of the iron and the large weight of gates and risers in relation to the casting itself, a blow will not separate the gates and risers. Consequently, most of the gates and risers must be cut off by machine. The cutting is done with a high-speed, motor-driven rotary wheel which "saws" through the gates and risers. The wheels are between 7 inches and 20 inches in diameter, ⅜ inch thick, and made of an abrasive-impregnated fiber material. Wear on the wheel is quite rapid. Cutting operations on 25 castings may wear as much as 4 inches off the diameter of the wheel. Wear rate for each casting depends primarily on the number and size of gates and risers.

The ductile iron castings produced in the foundry vary in size and shape so that it is necessary to have at least 16-inch-diameter wheels to reach the gates and risers on some castings, while wheels as small as 7 inches in diameter can be used on others. Wheels of less than 7-inch diameter are useless. The company can purchase wheels of three sizes—20, 16, and 10 inches—to use on their machines. They have one cutting machine capable of using 20-inch wheels, an additional machine capable of using 16-inch wheels, and several portable machines on which 10-inch wheels can be mounted.

As ductile iron assumed more prominence in the company's operations, attempts were made to utilize fully each wheel. The majority of castings can be cut off with either a 16- or 20-inch wheel. When a high production of ductile iron is undertaken both the 16- and 20-inch machines are used on the same type of casting. The company has developed a policy of purchasing only 20-inch wheels, and as they are worn down, to remove them from the 20-inch machine and pass them down to the 16-inch machine. After the wheels have worn to 12 or 13 inches, they are transferred to the 10-inch machines where they are used until the diameter is ground down to 7 inches, at which time the wheels are discarded. Following this policy, there should never be an excess of 16-inch wheels. The 10-inch wheels are not used as rapidly as the 16- and 20-inch wheels; hence, a surplus might appear over a period of time. There is no salvage value for the wheels at any time after they have been used. Wheels are checked out of the storeroom where records of inventory are kept. Notation is made when the wheels are checked out, by the order clerk. When the inventory drops to twenty-five or thirty wheels, the clerk initiates an order for 100

TABLE VII-1. RECORD OF ORDERS FOR 20-INCH WHEELS

Date Received		Size of Order	Value of Order	Inventory after Receipt of Order
1957	27 Aug.	71	$ 951	96
	12 Sept.	21	281	36
	13 Sept.	125	1675	161
	30 Oct.	20	268	20
	1 Nov.	50	670	55
	25 Nov.	58	777	59
	26 Nov.	50	670	50
	5 Dec.	51	683	51
	16 Dec.	40	536	40
	23 Dec.	44	589	44
1958	8 Jan.	42	563	49
	20 Jan.	54	724	54
	29 Jan.	44	590	74
	3 Feb.	49	657	111
	10 Feb.	54	724	151
	18 Feb.	47	630	167
	3 Mar.	91	1219	202
	21 Mar.	56	750	227
	31 Mar.	44	589	263
	21 Apr.	55	563	231
	4 June	103	1055	169
	16 July	107	1096	179
	22 Aug.	101	1034	102
	15 Sept.	101	1034	101
	29 Sept.	103	1055	146

TABLE VII-2. CHECK-OUT OF 20-INCH WHEELS

Date	Number of Wheels Checked Out	Date	Number of Wheels Checked Out
1958 21 May	7	11 Aug.	20
22	12	12	17
23	7	13	2
3 June	2	13	2
4	8	14	15
5	6	15	1
5	8	19	5
10	8	22	33
12	6	25	3
13	8	26	4
16	14	28	3
17	2	29	20
18	3	2 Sept.	6
19	12	3	20
20	6	8	4
24	5	8	4
25	11	11	7
VACATION		15	2
17 July	10	16	18
18	6	17	16
21	6	18	14
24	6	24	6
25	12	29	4
28	12	2 Oct.	7
29	15	3	6
30	15	6	10
31	6	8	2
1 Aug.	6	9	4
7	6		
8	18		

wheels. Wheels usually are received between three days and one week from the date the order is initiated. If a large run of ductile iron is expected, the re-order point is adjusted upward from twenty-five or thirty wheels. Wheels are received in packages of about seventeen wheels each. Some packages, however, might have only fifteen, and others could have as many as nineteen.

Mr. Pierce had assembled the following records:

Record of orders for 20-inch wheels (Table VII-1).

Check-out of 20-inch wheels (Table VII-2).

QUESTIONS

1. From an analysis of the time series, can you determine any patterns that aid in forecasting orders and minimizing inventory cost?

2. Does the frequency distribution of orders have a particular pattern related to generally known distributions, such as normal or Poisson?

3. Show a general formula expressing the total cost of ordering and carrying inventory of 20-inch wheels.

UNIMED DRUG COMPANY

Statistical Methods of Sales Forecasting for Production Planning

Sales of "Ivaway," the Unimed Drug Company's desensitizing drug for poison ivy exhibit a strong seasonal pattern, with heavy sales in the summer and poor sales during the remainder of the year. A record for the past years is shown in Table VII-3.

TABLE VII-3. MONTHLY SALES OF "IVAWAY" IN MILLIONS OF MILLIGRAMS

Month	1959	1960	1961
Jan.	10	2	12
Feb.	6	9	20
Mar.	8	10	30
Apr.	24	50	100
May	55	149	100
June	140	180	250
July	160	240	370
Aug.	280	300	490
Sept.	110	100	190
Oct.	55	24	13
Nov.	32	10	25
Dec.	5	2	15

Manufacturing facilities are limited, so that production for the peak season must start early, with gradual inventory buildups. It is undesirable to have excess inventories, because requirements in the slow winter can be met from current production. Moreover, "Ivaway" is a relatively unstable biological emulsion, which cannot be stored for over 8 months without losing potency. A sales forecast of two billion milligrams has been made for 1962.

QUESTIONS

Develop a method which will show the following:

1. The expected monthly sales throughout 1962, based on the seasonal pattern observed in prior years, and an annual total sale of 2 billion milligrams.

2. Any trend in the progress of actual sales indicative of the need for a revision in the original sales forecast of 2 billion.

3. The degree of confidence or the risk of error associated with the method used in 2 above.

Since Unimed must establish similar methods of prediction for many of its drugs, it is desirable to develop a method that permits easy calculations, visual presentation of observations and analyses, and minimum imposition of executive time of sales and production personnel.

CITIZENS BANK OF SOUTH BOSTON

Forecasting Time Deposits

Bank officials were interested in predicting the total amount of time deposits, that would be available during the coming year.

TABLE VII-4. SAVINGS DEPOSITS IN THOUSANDS

| | Year | | |
Month	1959	1960	1961
Jan.	2421.2	2635.6	2853.2
Feb.	2446.5	2694.5	2853.4
Mar.	2432.9	2717.8	2874.7
Apr.	2438.4	2696.3	2917.3
May	2471.0	2724.1	2935.3
June	2474.1	2725.3	2925.0
July	2479.9	2679.1	2936.5
Aug.	2459.2	2652.0	2827.8
Sept.	2450.5	2632.6	2831.9
Oct.	2446.6	2631.6	2854.7
Nov.	2538.0	2717.5	3001.2
Dec.	2595.9	2787.9	3080.1

Source: Citizens Bank of South Boston.

With full realization that the quality of the tobacco crop would be very influential, it being the dominant crop in the area served by the Bank, it was nevertheless considered desirable to analyze past time deposits for indications of what could be expected in the coming year.

One of the younger staff members compiled the data shown in Table VII-4 and prepared a tentative forecast of time-deposit expectations for the coming 12-month period.

QUESTIONS

Prepare the forecast for 1962.

EASTERN NATIONAL BANK

Forecasting Loan Portfolio Behavior

Trends in the volume of commercial loans and prospects of future behavior of the loan portfolio are matters of considerable consequence to many bankers. Such behavior influences not only the gross income and operating earnings of banks but also forecasts of income or expenditures, management of the securities portfolio, diversification within the loan portfolio, and the kinds of credit it may be desirable to extend.

Officers of the Eighteenth National Bank, located in a metropolitan area, were aware that 90 percent of the bank's loan portfolio of approximately 200 million dollars maintained a moderately close relationship to fluctuations of commercial loans, loans on securities, and real estate, and loans to finance companies in the banking system as a whole.

Mr. Guthrie, a well-informed vice president of the Eastern National Bank, was aware that a wide variety of business and economic factors influenced the action not only of total bank loans outstanding but also the movement of individual classifications of loans. It occurred to Mr. Guthrie that possibly some clue to the future behavior of the total of all bank loans outstanding, as well as of particular types of loans, might be gained by careful study of the action of the different kinds of loans issued over the past several years. The statistical series he considered most useful for this purpose was "Loans of Weekly Reporting Member Banks, in Leading Cities" as published in the *Federal Reserve Bulletin*. Mr. Guthrie asked the bank's research department to bring the pertinent figures together. The results of this request are shown in

TABLE VII-5. LOANS OF WEEKLY REPORTING MEMBER BANKS IN LEADING CITIES

Loans in 100 Million Dollars

Year	Month	Commercial	Securities*	Real Estate	Finance Companies
1956	March	267	38.4	83.0	NA
	June	280	37.3	85.6	"
	Sept.	291	31.5	87.8	"
	Dec.	305	33.0	88.6	"
1957	March	306	29.2	87.4	"
	June	315	30.5	86.7	"
	Sept.	319	28.5	87.1	"
	Dec.	316	31.5	87.7	"
1958	March	302	36.1	87.2	"
	June	296	45.4	88.6	"
	Sept.	296	30.1	91.2	"
	Dec.	304	34.6	95.7	"
1959	March	303	32.2	97.8	"
	June	320	35.2	102	38.3
	Sept.	295	34.2	125	39.5
	Dec.	305	39.2	127	44.5
1960	March**	310	27.4	126	40.7
	June	316	29.3	125	45.8
	Sept.	315	33.4	126	41.1
	Dec.	319	39.1	125	42.4
1961	March	320	30.8	124	33.6
	June	318	38.9	129	33.6
	Sept.	318	40.7	131	34.6
	Dec.	329	48.7	134	37.7

NA—not available.

* Includes loans to brokers, dealers, and others for purchasing or carrying securities.

** Beginning with 1960, monthly figures reported are based on the last week of each month.

Source: Federal Reserve Bulletin, "Weekly Reporting Member Banks, Assets and Liabilities of Banks in Leading Cities."

Table VII-5. Mr. Guthrie also thought that a forecast of this series for the next 12 months, in view of the general conformance of the bank's portfolio with the figures for the whole banking system, might give some clue to the behavior that could be expected in the bank's loan portfolio. Consequently, his next request to the research department was to extrapolate the figures in Table VII-5 to the end of the coming twelve-months' period.

QUESTIONS

Bring the figures in Table VII-3 as nearly up to date as the published material permits. In the light of this addition, and of any other material you consider relevant, you are to forecast the behavior of the several statistical series in the table quarter-by-quarter for the next 12 months and explain your reasoning.

Confine your report to 4 pages, double-spaced, and not more than three charts in addition to the completed Table VII-5.

HAWAIIAN TRANSPORTATION

Statistical Forecasting

The volume and character of the various types of transportation serving Hawaii directly reflect the pattern of economic activity of the islands. Without ocean freighter service to and from the mainland, it would be impossible to achieve the economic specialization necessary to maintain Hawaii's growing economy. Without the rapid expansion of airlines, the rise in tourism to present high levels could not have been achieved.

TABLE VII-6.   TRANSPORTATION GROWTH BY CATEGORIES
FISCAL YEARS 1950-1960

Year	Interisland Air Passengers	Transpacific Air Passengers	Interisland Surface Cargo, Revenue Tons	Transpacific Surface Cargo, Revenue Tons
1950	420,000	115,000	603	4566
1951	448,000	125,000	573	5124
1952	519,000	154,000	657	5461
1953	555,000	183,000	653	5607
1954	570,000	206,000	630	5412
1955	587,000	255,000	643	5402
1956	627,000	323,000	800	6073
1957	653,000	375,000	883	6367
1958	648,000	413,000	906	5683
1959	696,000	456,000	940	6099
1960	923,000	723,000	975	5867

Source: Annual Reports of the Hawaii Aeronautics Commission and the Board of Harbor Commissioners.

All interisland passenger traffic is by air, the most distant point being only one hour from Honolulu. The two interisland airlines, Aloha and Hawaiian, are an essential factor in coordinating business and community relationships between the islands so as to create a unified economy and state.

In a similar way the interisland barge service of Young Brothers provides for the interchange of goods.

In short, because of Hawaii's geographic position in the Central Pacific and because the state itself is broken down into island units, transportation is the "lifeline" of the economy.

QUESTIONS

Assume that you have been asked by the Hawaii Aeronautics Commission and the Board of Harbor Commissioners to forecast the future growth in the interisland and transpacific air passenger service and also the future growth in surface tonnage carried between the Hawaiian Islands and between Hawaii and the mainland. Make predictions needed to extend the data, which are going to be submitted to the next session of the legislature in conjunction with a request for an increase in appropriations by these two Commissions.

SUPERIOR INVESTMENTS, INCORPORATED

Statistical Analysis of Time Series

Superior Investments, Incorporated, was organized in the late 1930s as an investment company, specializing in relatively safe long-term growth stocks. Management of the fund, in recent weeks, had become increasingly interested in the future and potential of its life-insurance investments.

While it was realized that many factors affect the prospective growth, earning power, and profitability of life insurance stocks, it was nevertheless felt that as a preliminary step to a comprehensive review of the company's life-insurance investment program, an analysis of the following historical series might prove helpful:

1. Developments in the personal ownership of ordinary life insurance since 1940 in the United States.

2. Recent changes in attitudes towards ownership of life insurance, as reflected by past records of life insurance held per family in relation to its disposable income.

TABLE VII-7. LIFE INSURANCE AND DISPOSABLE PERSONAL INCOME

Year	Dollars of Life Insurance Owned, in Billions	Dollars of Life Insurance per Family, in 100's	Dollars of Disposable Personal Income per Family, in 100's
1940	79	27	17
1941	83	28	21
1942	85	28	26
1943	90	30	29
1944	95	31	32
1945	102	32	32
1946	113	36	34
1947	122	38	35
1948	131	42	39
1949	139	43	38
1950	149	46	41
1951	159	49	44
1952	171	53	46
1953	185	58	48
1954	198	63	48
1955	217	69	51
1956	238	76	54
1957	265	83	56
1958	288	88	57
1959	316	95	59
1960	340	102	62
1961			
1962			
1963			
1964			

Source: Spectator Year Book, Institute of Life Insurance, and U. S. Department of Commerce, as quoted in "Life Insurance Fact Book," by Institute of Life Insurance, New York 22, N. Y.

QUESTIONS

Using the data in Table VII-7, prepare an analysis of long-term trend and cyclical variation as regards the two points raised and make forecasts for the next five years, based on your analysis.

PRUDENTIAL INSURANCE COMPANY

Evaluation of Growth Rate of Business Volume

Growth in the amount of life insurance in force is evidenced by the following data for the Company:

Year	Millions	Year	Millions	Year	Millions
1945	$23,000	1951	$36,303	1957	$65,123
1946	26,072	1952	39,109	1958	70,524
1947	27,945	1953	43,185	1959	76,874
1948	29,635	1954	46,142	1960	82,200
1949	31,304	1955	51,557	1961	85,667
1950	34,102	1956	57,944	1962	

Source: National Underwriter Company, *Unique Manual.*

QUESTIONS

Comparing these growth figures against pertinent data, such as provided in Table VII-7 for Superior Investments Inc., evaluate the company's performance in increasing the amount of life insurance in force.

SELECTED BUSINESS INDEXES

Analysis of Economic Data

The time series in the table on p. 142 represent data on industrial production, construction, employment, department store sales, and consumer and wholesale prices in the United States, as published in the *Federal Reserve Bulletin* under "Business Activity, Selected Business Indexes."

Various economic analyses of trends, relationships, and fluctuations, as well as forecasts, can be prepared from this material.

SELECTED BUSINESS INDEXES

[1947–49 = 100, unless otherwise indicated]

Year or month	Industrial production — Total	Manufacturing	Mining	Utilities	Final products — Total	Consumer goods	Equipment	Materials	Construction contracts[1,2]	Nonagricultural employment total[3]	Manufacturing[4] — Employment	Manufacturing[4] — Payrolls	Freight carloadings[2]	Department store sales (retail value)	Consumer	Wholesale commodity
	Adj.	Adj.	Adj.	Adj.	Adj.	Adj.	Adj.	Adj.	Adj.	Adj.	Adj.	Unadj.	Adj.	Adj.	Unadj.	Unadj.
1948	103	103	106	101	102	101	105	104	41	101.6	102.8	105.0	127.6	104	83.8	87.9
1949	98	98	94	108	99	101	94	96	44	99.1	93.8	97.2	108.2	99	83.0	83.5
1950	113	114	105	123	112	115	102	114	61	102.4	99.7	111.7	117.1	107	83.8	86.8
1951	123	123	115	140	121	114	142	124	63	108.3	106.4	130.1	121.5	112	90.5	96.7
1952	127	127	114	152	130	116	170	125	67	110.5	106.3	137.0	115.0	114	92.5	94.0
1953	138	139	117	166	138	124	182	137	70	113.7	111.9	151.7	116.6	118	93.2	92.7
1954	130	129	113	178	132	123	161	128	76	111.0	102.0	138.4	104.6	118	93.6	92.9
1955	146	145	125	199	144	136	172	147	91	114.7	105.8	153.6	115.3	128	93.3	93.2
1956	151	150	132	218	150	139	188	151	92	118.6	106.9	162.4	115.9	135	94.7	96.2
1957	152	150	132	233	152	141	189	151	93	119.7	105.0	164.3	108.2	135	98.0	99.0
1958	141	139	120	244	145	140	165	138	102	116.4	95.5	151.5	93.8	136	100.7	100.4
1959	159	158	125	268	162	155	188	157	105	120.8	100.3	170.3	97.9	144	101.5	100.6
1960	164	163	128	287	168	161	195	160	105	123.0	100.0	172.8	95.3	146	103.1	100.7
1961	P165	P164	P129	....	P170	P164	P196	P161	108	122.4	95.9	170.5	91.2	149	104.2	100.3
1961—Mar.	156	153	127	291	162	156	188	150	104	121.2	94.4	160.3	88.0	146	103.9	101.0
Apr.	160	158	128	296	166	160	190	156	103	121.5	94.8	162.6	89.9	148	103.9	100.5
May	164	163	128	303	168	163	192	161	102	122.6	96.0	166.9	91.5	144	103.8	100.0
June	168	166	129	306	171	166	194	164	111	122.0	96.7	172.4	91.5	149	104.0	99.5
July	170	169	129	307	174	169	197	166	110	123.0	96.8	171.3	91.1	151	104.4	99.9
Aug.	172	170	130	314	174	169	198	168	116	123.0	96.3	174.4	91.8	150	104.3	100.1
Sept.	168	167	128	316	172	164	201	165	103	122.9	96.3	175.9	90.1	150	104.6	100.0
Oct.	171	170	131	317	175	168	203	168	114	122.9	96.5	179.1	94.4	151	104.6	100.0
Nov.	173	172	132	315	178	170	207	168	116	123.1	97.3	182.0	95.3	153	104.6	100.0
Dec.	174	173	133	314	179	172	208	170	119	123.3	97.6	182.0	95.6	156	104.5	100.4
1962—Jan.	172	171	130	318	r176	170	204	r168	115	123.2	97.1	175.9	93.9	149	104.5	100.8
Feb.	174	173	130	r319	178	170	r208	171	119	124.0	97.9	177.5	96.8	150	104.8	P100.7
Mar.	176	175	130	323	179	171	210	172	131	124.2	98.6	179.7	96.6	r157	105.0	100.7
Apr.	P178	P177	P134	P325	P181	P174	P212	P174	....	P124.7	P99.6	P182.0	96.1	e155	....	100.4

* Estimated. P Preliminary. r Revised.

Adj. = adjusted for seasonal variation. Unadj. = without seasonal adjustment.

1 Index from F. W. Dodge Corporation. Monthly index, seasonally adjusted, of dollar value of total construction contracts, including residential and nonresidential and heavy engineering.

2 Index 1957–59 = 100.

3 Employees only, excluding personnel in the armed forces.

4 Production workers only.

NOTE.—Indexes for employment (including Alaska and Hawaii, beginning with 1959) are compiled by the Federal Reserve from Bureau of Labor Statistics data. Payrolls and prices are compiled by the Bureau of Labor Statistics.

CENSUS BUREAU

Seasonal Variation in Labor Force Data

The table below shows total U. S. unemployment, obtained from the U. S. Census Bureau's monthly report on the labor force.

	Jan.	Feb.	Mar.	Apr.	May	June	July	Aug.	Sept.	Oct.	Nov.	Dec.
1940			8.36	8.23	7.99	8.31	9.15	8.74	6.85	7.24	7.26	6.91
1941	7.41	6.93	6.50	6.38	5.66	6.19	6.00	5.62	4.68	3.84	3.80	3.62
1942	4.32	4.04	3.58	3.05	2.59	2.89	2.83	2.19	1.68	1.61	1.63	1.52
1943	1.48	1.42	1.12	1.01	0.95	1.30	1.39	1.05	0.87	0.78	0.71	0.69
1944	0.81	0.69	0.69	0.63	0.73	0.88	0.89	0.68	0.60	0.44	0.50	0.50
1945	0.63	0.64	0.59	0.53	0.53	0.89	0.95	0.83	1.65	1.56	1.74	1.97
1946	2.30	2.65	2.70	2.33	2.31	2.57	2.27	2.06	2.07	1.96	1.93	2.12
1947	2.40	2.49	2.33	2.42	1.96	2.56	2.58	2.10	1.91	1.69	1.62	1.64
1948	2.06	2.64	2.44	2.19	1.76	2.18	2.23	1.94	1.90	1.64	1.83	1.94
1949	2.66	3.22	3.17	3.02	3.29	3.78	4.10	3.69	3.35	3.58	3.41	3.49
1950	4.48	4.68	4.12	3.52	3.06	3.38	3.21	2.50	2.34	1.94	2.24	2.23
1951	2.50	2.41	2.15	1.74	1.61	1.98	1.86	1.58	1.61	1.62	1.83	1.67
1952	2.05	2.09	1.80	1.61	1.60	1.82	1.94	1.60	1.44	1.28	1.42	1.42
1953	1.89	1.79	1.67	1.58	1.31	1.56	1.55	1.24	1.32	1.30	1.70	2.31
1954	3.09	3.67	3.72	3.46	3.30	3.35	3.35	3.24	3.10	2.74		

QUESTIONS

Prepare a seasonal index from the data and be prepared to discuss the usefulness of such an index.

Appendix

SQUARES, SQUARE ROOTS, AND RECIPROCALS

N	N²	√N	√10N	1000/N	N	N²	√N	√10N	1000/N
1	1	1.00 000	3.16 228	1000.00	50	2 500	7.07 107	22.36 07	20.00 00
2	4	1.41 421	4.47 214	500.00 0	51	2 601	7.14 143	22.58 32	19.60 78
3	9	1.73 205	5.47 723	333.33 3	52	2 704	7.21 110	22.80 35	19.23 08
4	16	2.00 000	6.32 456	250.00 0	53	2 809	7.28 011	23.02 17	18.86 79
5	25	2.23 607	7.07 107	200.00 0	54	2 916	7.34 847	23.23 79	18.51 85
					55	3 025	7.41 620	23.45 21	18.18 18
6	36	2.44 949	7.74 597	166.66 7	56	3 136	7.48 331	23.66 43	17.85 71
7	49	2.64 575	8.36 660	142.85 7	57	3 249	7.54 983	23.87 47	17.54 39
8	64	2.82 843	8.94 427	125.00 0	58	3 364	7.61 577	24.08 32	17.24 14
9	81	3.00 000	9.48 683	111.11 1	59	3 481	7.68 115	24.28 99	16.94 92
10	100	3.16 228	10.00 00	100.00 0	60	3 600	7.74 597	24.49 49	16.66 67
11	121	3.31 662	10.48 81	90.90 91	61	3 721	7.81 025	24.69 82	16.39 34
12	144	3.46 410	10.95 45	83.33 33	62	3 844	7.87 401	24.89 98	16.12 90
13	169	3.60 555	11.40 18	76.92 31	63	3 969	7.93 725	25.09 98	15.87 30
14	196	3.74 166	11.83 22	71.42 86	64	4 096	8.00 000	25.29 82	15.62 50
15	225	3.87 298	12.24 74	66.66 67	65	4 225	8.06 226	25.49 51	15.38 46
16	256	4.00 000	12.64 91	62.50 00	66	4 356	8.12 404	25.69 05	15.15 15
17	289	4.12 311	13.03 84	58.82 35	67	4 489	8.18 535	25.88 44	14.92 54
18	324	4.24 264	13.41 64	55.55 56	68	4 624	8.24 621	26.07 68	14.70 59
19	361	4.35 890	13.78 40	52.63 16	69	4 761	8.30 662	26.26 79	14.49 28
20	400	4.47 214	14.14 21	50.00 00	70	4 900	8.36 660	26.45 75	14.28 57
21	441	4.58 258	14.49 14	47.61 90	71	5 041	8.42 615	26.64 58	14.08 45
22	484	4.69 042	14.83 24	45.45 45	72	5 184	8.48 528	26.83 28	13.88 89
23	529	4.79 583	15.16 58	43.47 83	73	5 329	8.54 400	27.01 85	13.69 86
24	576	4.89 898	15.49 19	41.66 67	74	5 476	8.60 233	27.20 29	13.51 35
25	625	5.00 000	15.81 14	40.00 00	75	5 625	8.66 025	27.38 61	13.33 33
26	676	5.09 902	16.12 45	38.46 15	76	5 776	8.71 780	27.56 81	13.15 79
27	729	5.19 615	16.43 17	37.03 70	77	5 929	8.77 496	27.74 89	12.98 70
28	784	5.29 150	16.73 32	35.71 43	78	6 084	8.83 176	27.92 85	12.82 05
29	841	5.38 516	17.02 94	34.48 28	79	6 241	8.88 819	28.10 69	12.65 82
30	900	5.47 723	17.32 05	33.33 33	80	6 400	8.94 427	28.28 43	12.50 00
31	961	5.56 776	17.60 68	32.25 81	81	6 561	9.00 000	28.46 05	12.34 57
32	1 024	5.65 685	17.88 85	31.25 00	82	6 724	9.05 539	28.63 56	12.19 51
33	1 089	5.74 456	18.16 59	30.30 30	83	6 889	9.11 043	28.80 97	12.04 82
34	1 156	5.83 095	18.43 91	29.41 18	84	7 056	9.16 515	28.98 28	11.90 48
35	1 225	5.91 608	18.70 83	28.57 14	85	7 225	9.21 954	29.15 48	11.76 47
36	1 296	6.00 000	18.97 37	27.77 78	86	7 396	9.27 362	29.32 58	11.62 79
37	1 369	6.08 276	19.23 54	27.02 70	87	7 569	9.32 738	29.49 58	11.49 43
38	1 444	6.16 441	19.49 36	26.31 58	88	7 744	9.38 083	29.66 48	11.36 36
39	1 521	6.24 500	19.74 84	25.64 10	89	7 921	9.43 398	29.83 29	11.23 60
40	1 600	6.32 456	20.00 00	25.00 00	90	8 100	9.48 683	30.00 00	11.11 11
41	1 681	6.40 312	20.24 85	24.39 02	91	8 281	9.53 939	30.16 62	10.98 90
42	1 764	6.48 074	20.49 39	23.80 95	92	8 464	9.59 166	30.33 15	10.86 96
43	1 849	6.55 744	20.73 64	23.25 58	93	8 649	9.64 365	30.49 59	10.75 27
44	1 936	6.63 325	20.97 62	22.72 73	94	8 836	9.69 536	30.65 94	10.63 83
45	2 025	6.70 820	21.21 32	22.22 22	95	9 025	9.74 679	30.82 21	10.52 63
46	2 116	6.78 233	21.44 76	21.73 91	96	9 216	9.79 796	30.98 39	10.41 67
47	2 209	6.85 565	21.67 95	21.27 66	97	9 409	9.84 886	31.14 48	10.30 93
48	2 304	6.92 820	21.90 89	20.83 33	98	9 604	9.89 949	31.30 50	10.20 41
49	2 401	7.00 000	22.13 59	20.40 82	99	9 801	9.94 987	31.46 43	10.10 10
50	2 500	7.07 107	22.36 07	20.00 00	100	10 000	10.00 000	31.62 28	10.00 00
N	N²	√N	√10N	1000/N	N	N²	√N	√10N	1000/N

N	N²	√N	√10N	1000/N
100	10 000	10.00 00	31.62 28	10.00 000
101	10 201	10.04 99	31.78 05	9.90 099
102	10 404	10.09 95	31.93 74	9.80 392
103	10 609	10.14 89	32.09 36	9.70 874
104	10 816	10.19 80	32.24 90	9.61 538
105	11 025	10.24 70	32.40 37	9.52 381
106	11 236	10.29 56	32.55 76	9.43 396
107	11 449	10.34 41	32.71 09	9.34 579
108	11 664	10.39 23	32.86 34	9.25 926
109	11 881	10.44 03	33.01 51	9.17 431
110	12 100	10.48 81	33.16 62	9.09 091
111	12 321	10.53 57	33.31 67	9.00 901
112	12 544	10.58 30	33.46 64	8.92 857
113	12 769	10.63 01	33.61 55	8.84 956
114	12 996	10.67 71	33.76 39	8.77 193
115	13 225	10.72 38	33.91 16	8.69 565
116	13 456	10.77 03	34.05 88	8.62 069
117	13 689	10.81 67	34.20 55	8.54 701
118	13 924	10.86 28	34.35 11	8.47 458
119	14 161	10.90 87	34.49 64	8.40 336
120	14 400	10.95 45	34.64 10	8.33 333
121	14 641	11.00 00	34.78 51	8.26 446
122	14 884	11.04 54	34.92 85	8.19 672
123	15 129	11.09 05	35.07 14	8.13 008
124	15 376	11.13 55	35.21 36	8.06 452
125	15 625	11.18 03	35.35 53	8.00 000
126	15 876	11.22 50	35.49 65	7.93 651
127	16 129	11.26 94	35.63 71	7.87 402
128	16 384	11.31 37	35.77 71	7.81 250
129	16 641	11.35 78	35.91 66	7.75 194
130	16 900	11.40 18	36.05 55	7.69 231
131	17 161	11.44 55	36.19 39	7.63 359
132	17 424	11.48 91	36.33 18	7.57 576
133	17 689	11.53 26	36.46 92	7.51 880
134	17 956	11.57 58	36.60 60	7.46 269
135	18 225	11.61 90	36.74 23	7.40 741
136	18 496	11.66 19	36.87 82	7.35 294
137	18 769	11.70 47	37.01 35	7.29 927
138	19 044	11.74 73	37.14 84	7.24 638
139	19 321	11.78 98	37.28 27	7.19 424
140	19 600	11.83 22	37.41 66	7.14 286
141	19 881	11.87 43	37.55 00	7.09 220
142	20 164	11.91 64	37.68 29	7.04 225
143	20 449	11.95 83	37.81 53	6.99 301
144	20 736	12.00 00	37.94 73	6.94 444
145	21 025	12.04 16	38.07 89	6.89 655
146	21 316	12.08 30	38.20 99	6.84 932
147	21 609	12.12 44	38.34 06	6.80 272
148	21 904	12.16 55	38.47 08	6.75 676
149	22 201	12.20 66	38.60 05	6.71 141
150	22 500	12.24 74	38.72 98	6.66 667
N	N²	√N	√10N	1000/N

N	N²	√N	√10N	1000/N
150	22 500	12.24 74	38.72 98	6.66 667
151	22 801	12.28 82	38.85 87	6.62 252
152	23 104	12.32 88	38.98 72	6.57 895
153	23 409	12.36 93	39.11 52	6.53 595
154	23 716	12.40 97	39.24 28	6.49 351
155	24 025	12.44 99	39.37 00	6.45 161
156	24 336	12.49 00	39.49 68	6.41 026
157	24 649	12.53 00	39.62 32	6.36 943
158	24 964	12.56 98	39.74 92	6.32 911
159	25 281	12.60 95	39.87 48	6.28 931
160	25 600	12.64 91	40.00 00	6.25 000
161	25 921	12.68 86	40.12 48	6.21 118
162	26 244	12.72 79	40.24 92	6.17 284
163	26 569	12.76 71	40.37 33	6.13 497
164	26 896	12.80 62	40.49 69	6.09 756
165	27 225	12.84 52	40.62 02	6.06 061
166	27 556	12.88 41	40.74 31	6.02 410
167	27 889	12.92 28	40.86 56	5.98 802
168	28 224	12.96 15	40.98 78	5.95 238
169	28 561	13.00 00	41.10 96	5.91 716
170	28 900	13.03 84	41.23 11	5.88 235
171	29 241	13.07 67	41.35 21	5.84 795
172	29 584	13.11 49	41.47 29	5.81 395
173	29 929	13.15 29	41.59 33	5.78 035
174	30 276	13.19 09	41.71 33	5.74 713
175	30 625	13.22 88	41.83 30	5.71 429
176	30 976	13.26 65	41.95 24	5.68 182
177	31 329	13.30 41	42.07 14	5.64 972
178	31 684	13.34 17	42.19 00	5.61 798
179	32 041	13.37 91	42.30 84	5.58 659
180	32 400	13.41 64	42.42 64	5.55 556
181	32 761	13.45 36	42.54 41	5.52 486
182	33 124	13.49 07	42.66 15	5.49 451
183	33 489	13.52 77	42.77 85	5.46 448
184	33 856	13.56 47	42.89 52	5.43 478
185	34 225	13.60 15	43.01 16	5.40 541
186	34 596	13.63 82	43.12 77	5.37 634
187	34 969	13.67 48	43.24 35	5.34 759
188	35 344	13.71 13	43.35 90	5.31 915
189	35 721	13.74 77	43.47 41	5.29 101
190	36 100	13.78 40	43.58 90	5.26 316
191	36 481	13.82 03	43.70 35	5.23 560
192	36 864	13.85 64	43.81 78	5.20 833
193	37 249	13.89 24	43.93 18	5.18 135
194	37 636	13.92 84	44.04 54	5.15 464
195	38 025	13.96 42	44.15 88	5.12 821
196	38 416	14.00 00	44.27 19	5.10 204
197	38 809	14.03 57	44.38 47	5.07 614
198	39 204	14.07 12	44.49 72	5.05 051
199	39 601	14.10 67	44.60 94	5.02 513
200	40 000	14.14 21	44.72 14	5.00 000
N	N²	√N	√10N	1000/N

N	N²	√N	√10N	1000/N
200	40 000	14.14 21	44.72 14	5.00 000
201	40 401	14.17 74	44.83 30	4.97 512
202	40 804	14.21 27	44.94 44	4.95 050
203	41 209	14.24 78	45.05 55	4.92 611
204	41 616	14.28 29	45.16 64	4.90 196
205	42 025	14.31 78	45.27 69	4.87 805
206	42 436	14.35 27	45.38 72	4.85 437
207	42 849	14.38 75	45.49 73	4.83 092
208	43 264	14.42 22	45.60 70	4.80 769
209	43 681	14.45 68	45.71 65	4.78 469
210	44 100	14.49 14	45.82 58	4.76 190
211	44 521	14.52 58	45.93 47	4.73 934
212	44 944	14.56 02	46.04 35	4.71 698
213	45 369	14.59 45	46.15 19	4.69 484
214	45 796	14.62 87	46.26 01	4.67 290
215	46 225	14.66 29	46.36 81	4.65 116
216	46 656	14.69 69	46.47 58	4.62 963
217	47 089	14.73 09	46.58 33	4.60 829
218	47 524	14.76 48	46.69 05	4.58 716
219	47 961	14.79 86	46.79 74	4.56 621
220	48 400	14.83 24	46.90 42	4.54 545
221	48 841	14.86 61	47.01 06	4.52 489
222	49 284	14.89 97	47.11 69	4.50 450
223	49 729	14.93 32	47.22 29	4.48 430
224	50 176	14.96 66	47.32 86	4.46 429
225	50 625	15.00 00	47.43 42	4.44 444
226	51 076	15.03 33	47.53 95	4.42 478
227	51 529	15.06 65	47.64 45	4.40 529
228	51 984	15.09 97	47.74 93	4.38 596
229	52 441	15.13 27	47.85 39	4.36 681
230	52 900	15.16 58	47.95 83	4.34 783
231	53 361	15.19 87	48.06 25	4.32 900
232	53 824	15.23 15	48.16 64	4.31 034
233	54 289	15.26 43	48.27 01	4.29 185
234	54 756	15.29 71	48.37 35	4.27 350
235	55 225	15.32 97	48.47 68	4.25 532
236	55 696	15.36 23	48.57 98	4.23 729
237	56 169	15.39 48	48.68 26	4.21 941
238	56 644	15.42 72	48.78 52	4.20 168
239	57 121	15.45 96	48.88 76	4.18 410
240	57 600	15.49 19	48.98 98	4.16 667
241	58 081	15.52 42	49.09 18	4.14 938
242	58 564	15.55 63	49.19 35	4.13 223
243	59 049	15.58 85	49.29 50	4.11 523
244	59 536	15.62 05	49.39 64	4.09 836
245	60 025	15.65 25	49.49 75	4.08 163
246	60 516	15.68 44	49.59 84	4.06 504
247	61 009	15.71 62	49.69 91	4.04 858
248	61 504	15.74 80	49.79 96	4.03 226
249	62 001	15.77 97	49.89 99	4.01 606
250	62 500	15.81 14	50.00 00	4.00 000
N	N²	√N	√10N	1000/N

N	N²	√N	√10N	1000/N
250	62 500	15.81 14	50.00 00	4.00 000
251	63 001	15.84 30	50.09 99	3.98 406
252	63 504	15.87 45	50.19 96	3.96 825
253	64 009	15.90 60	50.29 91	3.95 257
254	64 516	15.93 74	50.39 84	3.93 701
255	65 025	15.96 87	50.49 75	3.92 157
256	65 536	16.00 00	50.59 64	3.90 625
257	66 049	16.03 12	50.69 52	3.89 105
258	66 564	16.06 24	50.79 37	3.87 597
259	67 081	16.09 35	50.89 20	3.86 100
260	67 600	16.12 45	50.99 02	3.84 615
261	68 121	16.15 55	51.08 82	3.83 142
262	68 644	16.18 64	51.18 59	3.81 679
263	69 169	16.21 73	51.28 35	3.80 228
264	69 696	16.24 81	51.38 09	3.78 788
265	70 225	16.27 88	51.47 82	3.77 358
266	70 756	16.30 95	51.57 52	3.75 940
267	71 289	16.34 01	51.67 20	3.74 532
268	71 824	16.37 07	51.76 87	3.73 134
269	72 361	16.40 12	51.86 52	3.71 747
270	72 900	16.43 17	51.96 15	3.70 370
271	73 441	16.46 21	52.05 77	3.69 004
272	73 984	16.49 24	52.15 36	3.67 647
273	74 529	16.52 27	52.24 94	3.66 300
274	75 076	16.55 29	52.34 50	3.64 964
275	75 625	16.58 31	52.44 04	3.63 636
276	76 176	16.61 32	52.53 57	3.62 319
277	76 729	16.64 33	52.63 08	3.61 011
278	77 284	16.67 33	52.72 57	3.59 712
279	77 841	16.70 33	52.82 05	3.58 423
280	78 400	16.73 32	52.91 50	3.57 143
281	78 961	16.76 31	53.00 94	3.55 872
282	79 524	16.79 29	53.10 37	3.54 610
283	80 089	16.82 26	53.19 77	3.53 357
284	80 656	16.85 23	53.29 17	3.52 113
285	81 225	16.88 19	53.38 54	3.50 877
286	81 796	16.91 15	53.47 90	3.49 650
287	82 369	16.94 11	53.57 24	3.48 432
288	82 944	16.97 06	53.66 56	3.47 222
289	83 521	17.00 00	53.75 87	3.46 021
290	84 100	17.02 94	53.85 16	3.44 828
291	84 681	17.05 87	53.94 44	3.43 643
292	85 264	17.08 80	54.03 70	3.42 466
293	85 849	17.11 72	54.12 95	3.41 297
294	86 436	17.14 64	54.22 18	3.40 136
295	87 025	17.17 56	54.31 39	3.38 983
296	87 616	17.20 47	54.40 59	3.37 838
297	88 209	17.23 37	54.49 77	3.36 700
298	88 804	17.26 27	54.58 94	3.35 570
299	89 401	17.29 16	54.68 09	3.34 448
300	90 000	17.32 05	54.77 23	3.33 333
N	N²	√N	√10N	1000/N

N	N²	√N	√10N	1000/N	N	N²	√N	√10N	1000/N
300	90 000	17.32 05	54.77 23	3.33 333	**350**	122 500	18.70 83	59.16 08	2.85 714
301	90 601	17.34 94	54.86 35	3.32 226	351	123 201	18.73 50	59.24 53	2.84 900
302	91 204	17.37 81	54.95 45	3.31 126	352	123 904	18.76 17	59.32 96	2.84 091
303	91 809	17.40 69	55.04 54	3.30 033	353	124 609	18.78 83	59.41 38	2.83 286
304	92 416	17.43 56	55.13 62	3.28 947	354	125 316	18.81 49	59.49 79	2.82 486
305	93 025	17.46 42	55.22 68	3.27 869	355	126 025	18.84 14	59.58 19	2.81 690
306	93 636	17.49 29	55.31 73	3.26 797	**356**	126 736	18.86 80	59.66 57	2.80 899
307	94 249	17.52 14	55.40 76	3.25 733	357	127 449	18.89 44	59.74 95	2.80 112
308	94 864	17.54 99	55.49 77	3.24 675	358	128 164	18.92 09	59.83 31	2.79 330
309	95 481	17.57 84	55.58 78	3.23 625	359	128 881	18.94 73	59.91 66	2.78 552
310	96 100	17.60 68	55.67 76	3.22 581	360	129 600	18.97 37	60.00 00	2.77 778
311	96 721	17.63 52	55.76 74	3.21 543	**361**	130 321	19.00 00	60.08 33	2.77 008
312	97 344	17.66 35	55.85 70	3.20 513	362	131 044	19.02 63	60.16 64	2.76 243
313	97 969	17.69 18	55.94 64	3.19 489	363	131 769	19.05 26	60.24 95	2.75 482
314	98 596	17.72 00	56.03 57	3.18 471	364	132 496	19.07 88	60.33 24	2.74 725
315	99 225	17.74 82	56.12 49	3.17 460	365	133 225	19.10 50	60.41 52	2.73 973
316	99 856	17.77 64	56.21 39	3.16 456	**366**	133 956	19.13 11	60.49 79	2.73 224
317	100 489	17.80 45	56.30 28	3.15 457	367	134 689	19.15 72	60.58 05	2.72 480
318	101 124	17.83 26	56.39 15	3.14 465	368	135 424	19.18 33	60.66 30	2.71 739
319	101 761	17.86 06	56.48 01	3.13 480	369	136 161	19.20 94	60.74 54	2.71 003
320	102 400	17.88 85	56.56 85	3.12 500	370	136 900	19.23 54	60.82 76	2.70 270
321	103 041	17.91 65	56.65 69	3.11 526	**371**	137 641	19.26 14	60.90 98	2.69 542
322	103 684	17.94 44	56.74 50	3.10 559	372	138 384	19.28 73	60.99 18	2.68 817
323	104 329	17.97 22	56.83 31	3.09 598	373	139 129	19.31 32	61.07 37	2.68 097
324	104 976	18.00 00	55.92 10	3.08 642	374	139 876	19.33 91	61.15 55	2.67 380
325	105 625	18.02 78	57.00 88	3.07 692	375	140 625	19.36 49	61.23 72	2.66 667
326	106 276	18.05 55	57.09 64	3.06 748	**376**	141 376	19.39 07	61.31 88	2.65 957
327	106 929	18.08 31	57.18 39	3.05 810	377	142 129	19.41 65	61.40 03	2.65 252
328	107 584	18.11 08	57.27 13	3.04 878	378	142 884	19.44 22	61.48 17	2.64 550
329	108 241	18.13 84	57.35 85	3.03 951	379	143 641	19.46 79	61.56 30	2.63 852
330	108 900	18.16 59	57.44 56	3.03 030	380	144 400	19.49 36	61.64 41	2.63 158
331	109 561	18.19 34	57.53 26	3.02 115	**381**	145 161	19.51 92	61.72 52	2.62 467
332	110 224	18.22 09	57.61 94	3.01 205	382	145 924	19.54 48	61.80 61	2.61 780
333	110 889	18.24 83	57.70 62	3.00 300	383	146 689	19.57 04	61.88 70	2.61 097
334	111 556	18.27 57	57.79 27	2.99 401	384	147 456	19.59 59	61.96 77	2.60 417
335	112 225	18.30 30	57.87 92	2.98 507	385	148 225	19.62 14	62.04 84	2.59 740
336	112 896	18.33 03	57.96 55	2.97 619	**386**	148 996	19.64 69	62.12 89	2.59 067
337	113 569	18.35 76	58.05 17	2.96 736	387	149 769	19.67 23	62.20 93	2.58 398
338	114 244	18.38 48	58.13 78	2.95 858	388	150 544	19.69 77	62.28 96	2.57 732
339	114 921	18.41 20	58.22 37	2.94 985	389	151 321	19.72 31	62.36 99	2.57 069
340	115 600	18 43 91	58.30 95	2.94 118	390	152 100	19.74 84	62.45 00	2.56 410
341	116 281	18.46 62	58.39 52	2.93 255	**391**	152 881	19.77 37	62.53 00	2.55 754
342	116 964	18.49 32	58.48 08	2.92 398	392	153 664	19.79 90	62.60 99	2.55 102
343	117 649	18.52 03	58.56 62	2.91 545	393	154 449	19.82 42	62.68 97	2.54 453
344	118 336	18.54 72	58.65 15	2.90 698	394	155 236	19.84 94	62.76 94	2.53 807
345	119 025	18.57 42	58.73 67	2.89 855	395	156 025	19.87 46	62.84 90	2.53 165
346	119 716	18.60 11	58.82 18	2.89 017	**396**	156 816	19.89 97	62.92 85	2.52 525
347	120 409	18.62 79	58.90 67	2.88 184	397	157 609	19.92 49	63.00 79	2.51 889
348	121 104	18.65 48	58.99 15	2.87 356	398	158 404	19.94 99	63.08 72	2.51 256
349	121 801	18.68 15	59.07 62	2.86 533	399	159 201	19.97 50	63.16 64	2.50 627
350	122 500	18.70 83	59.16 08	2.85 714	400	160 000	20.00 00	63.24 56	2.50 000
N	N²	√N	√10N	1000/N	N	N²	√N	√10N	1000/N

N	N²	√N	√10N	1000/N	N	N²	√N	√10N	1000/N
400	160 000	20.00 00	63.24 56	2.50 000	450	202 500	21.21 32	67.08 20	2.22 222
401	160 801	20.02 50	63.32 46	2.49 377	451	203 401	21.23 68	67.15 65	2.21 729
402	161 604	20.04 99	63.40 35	2.48 756	452	204 304	21.26 03	67.23 09	2.21 239
403	162 409	20.07 49	63.48 23	2.48 139	453	205 209	21.28 38	67.30 53	2.20 751
404	163 216	20.09 98	63.56 10	2.47 525	454	206 116	21.30 73	67.37 95	2.20 264
405	164 025	20.12 46	63.63 96	2.46 914	455	207 025	21.33 07	67.45 37	2.19 780
406	164 836	20.14 94	63.71 81	2.46 305	456	207 936	21.35 42	67.52 78	2.19 298
407	165 649	20.17 42	63.79 66	2.45 700	457	208 849	21.37 76	67.60 18	2.18 818
408	166 464	20.19 90	63.87 49	2.45 098	458	209 764	21.40 09	67.67 57	2.18 341
409	167 281	20.22 37	63.95 31	2.44 499	459	210 681	21.42 43	67.74 95	2.17 865
410	168 100	20.24 85	64.03 12	2.43 902	460	211 600	21.44 76	67.82 33	2.17 391
411	168 921	20.27 31	64.10 93	2.43 309	461	212 521	21.47 09	67.89 70	2.16 920
412	169 744	20.29 78	64.18 72	2.42 718	462	213 444	21.49 42	67.97 06	2.16 450
413	170 569	20.32 24	64.26 51	2.42 131	463	214 369	21.51 74	68.04 41	2.15 983
414	171 396	20.34 70	64.34 28	2.41 546	464	215 296	21.54 07	68.11 75	2.15 517
415	172 225	20.37 15	64.42 05	2.40 964	465	216 225	21.56 39	68.19 09	2.15 054
416	173 056	20.39 61	64.49 81	2.40 385	466	217 156	21.58 70	68.26 42	2.14 592
417	173 889	20.42 06	64.57 55	2.39 808	467	218 089	21.61 02	68.33 74	2.14 133
418	174 724	20.44 50	64.65 29	2.39 234	468	219 024	21.63 33	68.41 05	2.13 675
419	175 561	20.46 95	64.73 02	2.38 663	469	219 961	21.65 64	68.48 36	2.13 220
420	176 400	20.49 39	64.80 74	2.38 095	470	220 900	21.67 95	68.55 65	2.12 766
421	177 241	20.51 83	64.88 45	2.37 530	471	221 841	21.70 25	68.62 94	2.12 314
422	178 084	20.54 26	64.96 15	2.36 967	472	222 784	21.72 56	68.70 23	2.11 864
423	178 929	20.56 70	65.03 85	2.36 407	473	223 729	21.74 86	68.77 50	2.11 416
424	179 776	20.59 13	65.11 53	2.35 849	474	224 676	21.77 15	68.84 77	2.10 970
425	180 625	20.61 55	65.19 20	2.35 294	475	225 625	21.79 45	68.92 02	2.10 526
426	181 476	20.63 98	65.26 87	2.34 742	476	226 576	21.81 74	68.99 28	2.10 084
427	182 329	20.66 40	65.34 52	2.34 192	477	227 529	21.84 03	69.06 52	2.09 644
428	183 184	20.68 82	65.42 17	2.33 645	478	228 484	21.86 32	69.13 75	2.09 205
429	184 041	20.71 23	65.49 81	2.33 100	479	229 441	21.88 61	69.20 98	2.08 768
430	184 900	20.73 64	65.57 44	2.32 558	480	230 400	21.90 89	69.28 20	2.08 333
431	185 761	20.76 05	65.65 06	2.32 019	481	231 361	21.93 17	69.35 42	2.07 900
432	186 624	20.78 46	65.72 67	2.31 481	482	232 324	21.95 45	69.42 62	2.07 469
433	187 489	20.80 87	65.80 27	2.30 947	483	233 289	21.97 73	69.49 82	2.07 039
434	188 356	20.83 27	65.87 87	2.30 415	484	234 256	22.00 00	69.57 01	2.06 612
435	189 225	20.85 67	65.95 45	2.29 885	485	235 225	22.02 27	69.64 19	2.06 186
436	190 096	20.88 06	66.03 03	2.29 358	486	236 196	22.04 54	69.71 37	2.05 761
437	190 969	20.90 45	66.10 60	2.28 833	487	237 169	22.06 81	69.78 54	2.05 339
438	191 844	20.92 84	66.18 16	2.28 311	488	238 144	22.09 07	69.85 70	2.04 918
439	192 721	20.95 23	66.25 71	2.27 790	489	239 121	22.11 33	69.92 85	2.04 499
440	193 600	20.97 62	66.33 25	2.27 273	490	240 100	22.13 59	70.00 00	2.04 082
441	194 481	21.00 00	66.40 78	2.26 757	491	241 081	22.15 85	70.07 14	2.03 666
442	195 364	21.02 38	66.48 31	2.26 244	492	242 064	22.18 11	70.14 27	2.03 252
443	196 249	21.04 76	66.55 82	2.25 734	493	243 049	22.20 36	70.21 40	2.02 840
444	197 136	21.07 13	66.63 33	2.25 225	494	244 036	22.22 61	70.28 51	2.02 429
445	198 025	21.09 50	66.70 83	2.24 719	495	245 025	22.24 86	70.35 62	2.02 020
446	198 916	21.11 87	66.78 32	2.24 215	496	246 016	22.27 11	70.42 73	2.01 613
447	199 809	21.14 24	66.85 81	2.23 714	497	247 009	22.29 35	70.49 82	2.01 207
448	200 704	21.16 60	66.93 28	2.23 214	498	248 004	22.31 59	70.56 91	2.00 803
449	201 601	21.18 96	67.00 75	2.22 717	499	249 001	22.33 83	70.63 99	2.00 401
450	202 500	21.21 32	67.08 20	2.22 222	500	250 000	22.36 07	70.71 07	2.00 000
N	N²	√N	√10N	1000/N	N	N²	√N	√10N	1000/N

N	N²	√N	√10N	1000 /N
500	250 000	22.36 07	70.71 07	2.00 000
501	251 001	22.38 30	70.78 14	1.99 601
502	252 004	22.40 54	70.85 20	1.99 203
503	253 009	22.42 77	70.92 25	1.98 807
504	254 016	22.44 99	70.99 30	1.98 413
505	255 025	22.47 22	71.06 34	1.98 020
506	256 036	22.49 44	71.13 37	1.97 628
507	257 049	22.51 67	71.20 39	1.97 239
508	258 064	22.53 89	71.27 41	1.96 850
509	259 081	22.56 10	71.34 42	1.96 464
510	260 100	22.58 32	71.41 43	1.96 078
511	261 121	22.60 53	71.48 43	1.95 695
512	262 144	22.62 74	71.55 42	1.95 312
513	263 169	22.64 95	71.62 40	1.94 932
514	264 196	22.67 16	71.69 38	1.94 553
515	265 225	22.69 36	71.76 35	1.94 175
516	266 256	22.71 56	71.83 31	1.93 798
517	267 289	22.73 76	71.90 27	1.93 424
518	268 324	22.75 96	71.97 22	1.93 050
519	269 361	22.78 16	72.04 17	1.92 678
520	270 400	22.80 35	72.11 10	1.92 308
521	271 441	22.82 54	72.18 03	1.91 939
522	272 484	22.84 73	72.24 96	1.91 571
523	273 529	22.86 92	72.31 87	1.91 205
524	274 576	22.89 10	72.38 78	1.90 840
525	275 625	22.91 29	72.45 69	1.90 476
526	276 676	22.93 47	72.52 59	1.90 114
527	277 729	22.95 65	72.59 48	1.89 753
528	278 784	22.97 83	72.66 36	1.89 394
529	279 841	23.00 00	72.73 24	1.89 036
530	280 900	23.02 17	72.80 11	1.88 679
531	281 961	23.04 34	72.86 97	1.88 324
532	283 024	23.06 51	72.93 83	1.87 970
533	284 089	23.08 68	73.00 68	1.87 617
534	285 156	23.10 84	73.07 53	1.87 266
535	286 225	23.13 01	73.14 37	1.86 916
536	287 296	23.15 17	73.21 20	1.86 567
537	288 369	23.17 33	73.28 03	1.86 220
538	289 444	23.19 48	73.34 85	1.85 874
539	290 521	23.21 64	73.41 66	1.85 529
540	291 600	23.23 79	73.48 47	1.85 185
541	292 681	23.25 94	73.55 27	1.84 843
542	293 764	23.28 09	73.62 06	1.84 502
543	294 849	23.30 24	73.68 85	1.84 162
544	295 936	23.32 38	73.75 64	1.83 824
545	297 025	23.34 52	73.82 41	1.83 486
546	298 116	23.36 66	73.89 18	1.83 150
547	299 209	23.38 80	73.95 94	1.82 815
548	300 304	23.40 94	74.02 70	1.82 482
549	301 401	23.43 07	74.09 45	1.82 149
550	302 500	23.45 21	74.16 20	1.81 818

N	N²	√N	√10N	1000 /N
550	302 500	23.45 21	74.16 20	1.81 818
551	303 601	23.47 34	74.22 94	1.81 488
552	304 704	23.49 47	74.29 67	1.81 159
553	305 809	23.51 60	74.36 40	1.80 832
554	306 916	23.53 72	74.43 12	1.80 505
555	308 025	23.55 84	74.49 83	1.80 180
556	309 136	23.57 97	74.56 54	1.79 856
557	310 249	23.60 08	74.63 24	1.79 533
558	311 364	23.62 20	74.69 94	1.79 211
559	312 481	23.64 32	74.76 63	1.78 891
560	313 600	23.66 43	74.83 31	1.78 571
561	314 721	23.68 54	74.89 99	1.78 253
562	315 844	23.70 65	74.96 67	1.77 936
563	316 969	23.72 76	75.03 33	1.77 620
564	318 096	23.74 87	75.09 99	1.77 305
565	319 225	23.76 97	75.16 65	1.76 991
566	320 356	23.79 08	75.23 30	1.76 678
567	321 489	23.81 18	75.29 94	1.76 367
568	322 624	23.83 28	75.36 58	1.76 056
569	323 761	23.85 37	75.43 21	1.75 747
570	324 900	23.87 47	75.49 83	1.75 439
571	326 041	23.89 56	75.56 45	1.75 131
572	327 184	23.91 65	75.63 07	1.74 825
573	328 329	23.93 74	75.69 68	1.74 520
574	329 476	23.95 83	75.76 28	1.74 216
575	330 625	23.97 92	75.82 88	1.73 913
576	331 776	24.00 00	75.89 47	1.73 611
577	332 929	24.02 08	75.96 05	1.73 310
578	334 084	24.04 16	76.02 63	1.73 010
579	335 241	24.06 24	76.09 20	1.72 712
580	336 400	24.08 32	76.15 77	1.72 414
581	337 561	24.10 39	76.22 34	1.72 117
582	338 724	24.12 47	76.28 89	1.71 821
583	339 889	24.14 54	76.35 44	1.71 527
584	341 056	24.16 61	76.41 99	1.71 233
585	342 225	24.18 68	76.48 53	1.70 940
586	343 396	24.20 74	76.55 06	1.70 648
587	344 569	24.22 81	76.61 59	1.70 358
588	345 744	24.24 87	76.68 12	1.70 068
589	346 921	24.26 93	76.74 63	1.69 779
590	348 100	24.28 99	76.81 15	1.69 492
591	349 281	24.31 05	76.87 65	1.69 205
592	350 464	24.33 11	76.94 15	1.68 919
593	351 649	24.35 16	77.00 65	1.68 634
594	352 836	24.37 21	77.07 14	1.68 350
595	354 025	24.39 26	77.13 62	1.68 067
596	355 216	24.41 31	77.20 10	1.67 785
597	356 409	24.43 36	77.26 58	1.67 504
598	357 604	24.45 40	77.33 05	1.67 224
599	358 801	24.47 45	77.39 51	1.66 945
600	360 000	24.49 49	77.45 97	1.66 667

N	N²	√N	√10N	1000 /N
600	360 000	24.49 49	77.45 97	1.66 667
601	361 201	24.51 53	77.52 42	1.66 389
602	362 404	24.53 57	77.58 87	1.66 113
603	363 609	24.55 61	77.65 31	1.65 837
604	364 816	24.57 64	77.71 74	1.65 563
605	366 025	24.59 67	77.78 17	1.65 289
606	367 236	24.61 71	77.84 60	1.65 017
607	368 449	24.63 74	77.91 02	1.64 745
608	369 664	24.65 77	77.97 44	1.64 474
609	370 881	24.67 79	78.03 85	1.64 204
610	372 100	24.69 82	78.10 25	1.63 934
611	373 321	24.71 84	78.16 65	1.63 666
612	374 544	24.73 86	78.23 04	1.63 399
613	375 769	24.75 88	78.29 43	1.63 132
614	376 996	24.77 90	78.35 82	1.62 866
615	378 225	24.79 92	78.42 19	1.62 602
616	379 456	24.81 93	78.48 57	1.62 338
617	380 689	24.83 95	78.54 93	1.62 075
618	381 924	24.85 96	78.61 30	1.61 812
619	383 161	24.87 97	78.67 66	1.61 551
620	384 400	24.89 98	78.74 01	1.61 290
621	385 641	24.91 99	78.80 36	1.61 031
622	386 884	24.93 99	78.86 70	1.60 772
623	388 129	24.96 00	78.93 03	1.60 514
624	389 376	24.98 00	78.99 37	1.60 256
625	390 625	25.00 00	79.05 69	1.60 000
626	391 876	25.02 00	79.12 02	1.59 744
627	393 129	25.04 00	79.18 33	1.59 490
628	394 384	25.05 99	79.24 65	1.59 236
629	395 641	25.07 99	79.30 95	1.58 983
630	396 900	25.09 98	79.37 25	1.58 730
631	398 161	25.11 97	79.43 55	1.58 479
632	399 424	25.13 96	79.49 84	1.58 228
633	400 689	25.15 95	79.56 13	1.57 978
634	401 956	25.17 94	79.62 41	1.57 729
635	403 225	25.19 92	79.68 69	1.57 480
636	404 496	25.21 90	79.74 96	1.57 233
637	405 769	25.23 89	79.81 23	1.56 986
638	407 044	25.25 87	79.87 49	1.56 740
639	408 321	25.27 84	79.93 75	1.56 495
640	409 600	25.29 82	80.00 00	1.56 250
641	410 881	25.31 80	80.06 25	1.56 006
642	412 164	25.33 77	80.12 49	1.55 763
643	413 449	25.35 74	80.18 73	1.55 521
644	414 736	25.37 72	80.24 96	1.55 280
645	416 025	25.39 69	80.31 19	1.55 039
646	417 316	25.41 65	80.37 41	1.54 799
647	418 609	25.43 62	80.43 63	1.54 560
648	419 904	25.45 58	80.49 84	1.54 321
649	421 201	25.47 55	80.56 05	1.54 083
650	422 500	25.49 51	80.62 26	1.53 846
N	N²	√N	√10N	1000 /N

N	N²	√N	√10N	1000 /N
650	422 500	25.49 51	80.62 26	1.53 846
651	423 801	25.51 47	80.68 46	1.53 610
652	425 104	25.53 43	80.74 65	1.53 374
653	426 409	25.55 39	80.80 84	1.53 139
654	427 716	25.57 34	80.87 03	1.52 905
655	429 025	25.59 30	80.93 21	1.52 672
656	430 336	25.61 25	80.99 38	1.52 439
657	431 649	25.63 20	81.05 55	1.52 207
658	432 964	25.65 15	81.11 72	1.51 976
659	434 281	25.67 10	81.17 88	1.51 745
660	435 600	25.69 05	81.24 04	1.51 515
661	436 921	25.70 99	81.30 19	1.51 286
662	438 244	25.72 94	81.36 34	1.51 057
663	439 569	25.74 88	81.42 48	1.50 830
664	440 896	25.76 82	81.48 62	1.50 602
665	442 225	25.78 76	81.54 75	1.50 376
666	443 556	25.80 70	81.60 88	1.50 150
667	444 889	25.82 63	81.67 01	1.49 925
668	446 224	25.84 57	81.73 13	1.49 701
669	447 561	25.86 50	81.79 24	1.49 477
670	448 900	25.88 44	81.85 35	1.49 254
671	450 241	25.90 37	81.91 46	1.49 031
672	451 584	25.92 30	81.97 56	1.48 810
673	452 929	25.94 22	82.03 66	1.48 588
674	454 276	25.96 15	82.09 75	1.48 368
675	455 625	25.98 08	82.15 84	1.48 148
676	456 976	26.00 00	82.21 92	1.47 929
677	458 329	26.01 92	82.28 00	1.47 710
678	459 684	26.03 84	82.34 08	1.47 493
679	461 041	26.05 76	82.40 15	1.47 275
680	462 400	26.07 68	82.46 21	1.47 059
681	463 761	26.09 60	82.52 27	1.46 843
682	465 124	26.11 51	82.58 33	1.46 628
683	466 489	26.13 43	82.64 38	1.46 413
684	467 856	26.15 34	82.70 43	1.46 199
685	469 225	26.17 25	82.76 47	1.45 985
686	470 596	26.19 16	82.82 51	1.45 773
687	471 969	26.21 07	82.88 55	1.45 560
688	473 344	26.22 98	82.94 58	1.45 349
689	474 721	26.24 88	83.00 60	1.45 138
690	476 100	26.26 79	83.06 62	1.44 928
691	477 481	26.28 69	83.12 64	1.44 718
692	478 864	26.30 59	83.18 65	1.44 509
693	480 249	26.32 49	83.24 66	1.44 300
694	481 636	26.34 39	83.30 67	1.44 092
695	483 025	26.36 29	83.36 67	1.43 885
696	484 416	26.38 18	83.42 66	1.43 678
697	485 809	26.40 08	83.48 65	1.43 472
698	487 204	26.41 97	83.54 64	1.43 266
699	488 601	26.43 86	83.60 62	1.43 062
700	490 000	26.45 75	83.66 60	1.42 857
N	N²	√N	√10N	1000 /N

N	N²	√N	√10N	1000/N	N	N²	√N	√10N	1000/N
700	490 000	26.45 75	83.66 60	1.42 857	750	562 500	27.38 61	86.60 25	1.33 333
701	491 401	26.47 64	83.72 57	1.42 653	751	564 001	27.40 44	86.66 03	1.33 156
702	492 804	26.49 53	83.78 54	1.42 450	752	565 504	27.42 26	86.71 79	1.32 979
703	494 209	26.51 41	83.84 51	1.42 248	753	567 009	27.44 08	86.77 56	1.32 802
704	495 616	26.53 30	83.90 47	1.42 045	754	568 516	27.45 91	86.83 32	1.32 626
705	497 025	26.55 18	83.96 43	1.41 844	755	570 025	27.47 73	86.89 07	1.32 450
706	498 436	26.57 07	84.02 38	1.41 643	756	571 536	27.49 55	86.94 83	1.32 275
707	499 849	26.58 95	84.08 33	1.41 443	757	573 049	27.51 36	87.00 57	1.32 100
708	501 264	26.60 83	84.14 27	1.41 243	758	574 564	27.53 18	87.06 32	1.31 926
709	502 681	26.62 71	84.20 21	1.41 044	759	576 081	27.55 00	87.12 06	1.31 752
710	504 100	26.64 58	84.26 15	1.40 845	760	577 600	27.56 81	87.17 80	1.31 579
711	505 521	26.66 46	84.32 08	1.40 647	761	579 121	27.58 62	87.23 53	1.31 406
712	506 944	26.68 33	84.38 01	1.40 449	762	580 644	27.60 43	87.29 26	1.31 234
713	508 369	26.70 21	84.43 93	1.40 252	763	582 169	27.62 25	87.34 99	1.31 062
714	509 796	26.72 08	84.49 85	1.40 056	764	583 696	27.64 05	87.40 71	1.30 890
715	511 225	26.73 95	84.55 77	1.39 860	765	585 225	27.65 86	87.46 43	1.30 719
716	512 656	26.75 82	84.61 68	1.39 665	766	586 756	27.67 67	87.52 14	1.30 548
717	514 089	26.77 69	84.67 59	1.39 470	767	588 289	27.69 48	87.57 85	1.30 378
718	515 524	26.79 55	84.73 49	1.39 276	768	589 824	27.71 28	87.63 56	1.30 208
719	516 961	26.81 42	84.79 39	1.39 082	769	591 361	27.73 08	87.69 26	1.30 039
720	518 400	26.83 28	84.85 28	1.38 889	770	592 900	27.74 89	87.74 96	1.29 870
721	519 841	26.85 14	84.91 17	1.38 696	771	594 441	27.76 69	87.80 66	1.29 702
722	521 284	26.87 01	84.97 06	1.38 504	772	595 984	27.78 49	87.86 35	1.29 534
723	522 729	26.88 87	85.02 94	1.38 313	773	597 529	27.80 29	87.92 04	1.29 366
724	524 176	26.90 72	85.08 82	1.38 122	774	599 076	27.82 09	87.97 73	1.29 199
725	525 625	26.92 58	85.14 69	1.37 931	775	600 625	27.83 88	88.03 41	1.29 032
726	527 076	26.94 44	85.20 56	1.37 741	776	602 176	27.85 68	88.09 09	1.28 866
727	528 529	26.96 29	85.26 43	1.37 552	777	603 729	27.87 47	88.14 76	1.28 700
728	529 984	26.98 15	85.32 29	1.37 363	778	605 284	27.89 27	88.20 43	1.28 535
729	531 441	27.00 00	85.38 15	1.37 174	779	606 841	27.91 06	88.26 10	1.28 370
730	532 900	27.01 85	85.44 00	1.36 986	780	608 400	27.92 85	88.31 76	1.28 205
731	534 361	27.03 70	85.49 85	1.36 799	781	609 961	27.94 64	88.37 42	1.28 041
732	535 824	27.05 55	85.55 70	1.36 612	782	611 524	27.96 43	88.43 08	1.27 877
733	537 289	27.07 40	85.61 54	1.36 426	783	613 089	27.98 21	88.48 73	1.27 714
734	538 756	27.09 24	85.67 38	1.36 240	784	614 656	28.00 00	88.54 38	1.27 551
735	540 225	27.11 09	85.73 21	1.36 054	785	616 225	28.01 79	88.60 02	1.27 389
736	541 696	27.12 93	85.79 04	1.35 870	786	617 796	28.03 57	88.65 66	1.27 226
737	543 169	27.14 77	85.84 87	1.35 685	787	619 369	28.05 35	88.71 30	1.27 065
738	544 644	27.16 62	85.90 69	1.35 501	788	620 944	28.07 13	88.76 94	1.26 904
739	546 121	27.18 46	85.96 51	1.35 318	789	622 521	28.08 91	88.82 57	1.26 743
740	547 600	27.20 29	86.02 33	1.35 135	790	624 100	28.10 69	88.88 19	1.26 582
741	549 081	27.22 13	86.08 14	1.34 953	791	625 681	28.12 47	88.93 82	1.26 422
742	550 564	27.23 97	86.13 94	1.34 771	792	627 264	28.14 25	88.99 44	1.26 263
743	552 049	27.25 80	86.19 74	1.34 590	793	628 849	28.16 03	89.05 05	1.26 103
744	553 536	27.27 64	86.25 54	1.34 409	794	630 436	28.17 80	89.10 67	1.25 945
745	555 025	27.29 47	86.31 34	1.34 228	795	632 025	28.19 57	89.16 28	1.25 786
746	556 516	27.31 30	86.37 13	1.34 048	796	633 616	28.21 35	89.21 88	1.25 628
747	558 009	27.33 13	86.42 92	1.33 869	797	635 209	28.23 12	89.27 49	1.25 471
748	559 504	27.34 96	86.48 70	1.33 690	798	636 804	28.24 89	89.33 08	1.25 313
749	561 001	27.36 79	86.54 48	1.33 511	799	638 401	28.26 66	89.38 68	1.25 156
750	562 500	27.38 61	86.60 25	1.33 333	800	640 000	28.28 43	89.44 27	1.25 000
N	N²	√N	√10N	1000/N	N	N²	√N	√10N	1000/N

N	N²	√N	√10N	1000/N
800	640 000	28.28 43	89.44 27	1.25 000
801	641 601	28.30 19	89.49 86	1.24 844
802	643 204	28.31 96	89.55 45	1.24 688
803	644 809	28.33 73	89.61 03	1.24 533
804	646 416	28.35 49	89.66 60	1.24 378
805	648 025	28.37 25	89.72 18	1.24 224
806	649 636	28.39 01	89.77 75	1.24 069
807	651 249	28.40 77	89.83 32	1.23 916
808	652 864	28.42 53	89.88 88	1.23 762
809	654 481	28.44 29	89.94 44	1.23 609
810	656 100	28.46 05	90.00 00	1.23 457
811	657 721	28.47 81	90.05 55	1.23 305
812	659 344	28.49 56	90.11 10	1.23 153
813	660 969	28.51 32	90.16 65	1.23 001
814	662 596	28.53 07	90.22 19	1.22 850
815	664 225	28.54 82	90.27 74	1.22 699
816	665 856	28.56 57	90.33 27	1.22 549
817	667 489	28.58 32	90.38 81	1.22 399
818	669 124	28.60 07	90.44 34	1.22 249
819	670 761	28.61 82	90.49 86	1.22 100
820	672 400	28.63 56	90.55 39	1.21 951
821	674 041	28.65 31	90.60 91	1.21 803
822	675 684	28.67 05	90.66 42	1.21 655
823	677 329	28.68 80	90.71 93	1.21 507
824	678 976	28.70 54	90.77 44	1.21 359
825	680 625	28.72 28	90.82 95	1.21 212
826	682 276	28.74 02	90.88 45	1.21 065
827	683 929	28.75 76	90.93 95	1.20 919
828	685 584	28.77 50	90.99 45	1.20 773
829	687 241	28.79 24	91.04 94	1.20 627
830	688 900	28.80 97	91.10 43	1.20 482
831	690 561	28.82 71	91.15 92	1.20 337
832	692 224	28.84 44	91.21 40	1.20 192
833	693 889	28.86 17	91.26 88	1.20 048
834	695 556	28.87 91	91.32 36	1.19 904
835	697 225	28.89 64	91.37 83	1.19 760
836	698 896	28.91 37	91.43 30	1.19 617
837	700 569	28.93 10	91.48 77	1.19 474
838	702 244	28.94 82	91.54 23	1.19 332
839	703 921	28.96 55	91.59 69	1.19 190
840	705 600	28.98 28	91.65 15	1.19 048
841	707 281	29.00 00	91.70 61	1.18 906
842	708 964	29.01 72	91.76 06	1.18 765
843	710 649	29.03 45	91.81 50	1.18 624
844	712 336	29.05 17	91.86 95	1.18 483
845	714 025	29.06 89	91.92 39	1.18 343
846	715 716	29.08 61	91.97 83	1.18 203
847	717 409	29.10 33	92.03 26	1.18 064
848	719 104	29.12 04	92.08 69	1.17 925
849	720 801	29.13 76	92.14 12	1.17 786
850	722 500	29.15 48	92.19 54	1.17 647
N	N²	√N	√10N	1000/N

N	N²	√N	√10N	1000/N
850	722 500	29.15 48	92.19 54	1.17 647
851	724 201	29.17 19	92.24 97	1.17 509
852	725 904	29.18 90	92.30 38	1.17 371
853	727 609	29.20 62	92.35 80	1.17 233
854	729 316	29.22 33	92.41 21	1.17 096
855	731 025	29.24 04	92.46 62	1.16 959
856	732 736	29.25 75	92.52 03	1.16 822
857	734 449	29.27 46	92.57 43	1.16 686
858	736 164	29.29 16	92.62 83	1.16 550
859	737 881	29.30 87	92.68 23	1.16 414
860	739 600	29.32 58	92.73 62	1.16 279
861	741 321	29.34 28	92.79 01	1.16 144
862	743 044	29.35 98	92.84 40	1.16 009
863	744 769	29.37 69	92.89 78	1.15 875
864	746 496	29.39 39	92.95 16	1.15 741
865	748 225	29.41 09	93.00 54	1.15 607
866	749 956	29.42 79	93.05 91	1.15 473
867	751 689	29.44 49	93.11 28	1.15 340
868	753 424	29.46 18	93.16 65	1.15 207
869	755 161	29.47 88	93.22 02	1.15 075
870	756 900	29.49 58	93.27 38	1.14 943
871	758 641	29.51 27	93.32 74	1.14 811
872	760 384	29.52 96	93.38 09	1.14 679
873	762 129	29.54 66	93.43 45	1.14 548
874	763 876	29.56 35	93.48 80	1.14 416
875	765 625	29.58 04	93.54 14	1.14 286
876	767 376	29.59 73	93.59 49	1.14 155
877	769 129	29.61 42	93.64 83	1.14 025
878	770 884	29.63 11	93.70 17	1.13 895
879	772 641	29.64 79	93.75 50	1.13 766
880	774 400	29.66 48	93.80 83	1.13 636
881	776 161	29.68 16	93.86 16	1.13 507
882	777 924	29.69 85	93.91 49	1.13 379
883	779 689	29.71 53	93.96 81	1.13 250
884	781 456	29.73 21	94.02 13	1.13 122
885	783 225	29.74 89	94.07 44	1.12 994
886	784 996	29.76 58	94.12 76	1:12 867
887	786 769	29.78 25	94.18 07	1.12 740
888	788 544	29.79 93	94.23 38	1.12 613
889	790 321	29.81 61	94.28 68	1.12 486
890	792 100	29.83 29	94.33 98	1.12 360
891	793 881	29.84 96	94.39 28	1.12 233
892	795 664	29.86 64	94.44 58	1.12 108
893	797 449	29.88 31	94.49 87	1.11 982
894	799 236	29.89 98	94.55 16	1.11 857
895	801 025	29.91 66	94.60 44	1.11 732
896	802 816	29.93 33	94.65 73	1.11 607
897	804 609	29.95 00	94.71 01	1.11 483
898	806 404	29.96 66	94.76 29	1.11 359
899	808 201	29.98 33	94.81 56	1.11 235
900	810 000	30.00 00	94.86 83	1.11 111
N	N²	√N	√10N	1000/N

N	N²	√N	√10N	1000 /N
900	810 000	30.00 00	94.86 83	1.11 111
901	811 801	30.01 67	94.92 10	1.10 988
902	813 604	30.03 33	94.97 37	1.10 865
903	815 409	30.05 00	95.02 63	1.10 742
904	817 216	30.06 66	95.07 89	1.10 619
905	819 025	30.08 32	95.13 15	1.10 497
906	820 836	30.09 98	95.18 40	1.10 375
907	822 649	30.11 64	95.23 65	1.10 254
908	824 464	30.13 30	95.28 90	1.10 132
909	826 281	30.14 96	95.34 15	1.10 011
910	828 100	30.16 62	95.39 39	1.09 890
911	829 921	30.18 28	95.44 63	1.09 769
912	831 744	30.19 93	95.49 87	1.09 649
913	833 569	30.21 59	95.55 10	1.09 529
914	835 396	30.23 24	95.60 33	1.09 409
915	837 225	30.24 90	95.65 56	1.09 290
916	839 056	30.26 55	95.70 79	1.09 170
917	840 889	30.28 20	95.76 01	1 09 051
918	842 724	30.29 85	95.81 23	1.08 932
919	844 561	30.31 50	95.86 45	1.08 814
920	846 400	30.33 15	95.91 66	1.08 696
921	848 241	30.34 80	95.96 87	1.08 578
922	850 084	30.36 45	96.02 08	1.08 460
923	851 929	30.38 09	96.07 29	1.08 342
924	853 776	30.39 74	96.12 49	1.08 225
925	855 625	30.41 38	96.17 69	1.08 108
926	857 476	30.43 02	96.22 89	1.07 991
927	859 329	30.44 67	96.28 08	1.07 875
928	861 184	30.46 31	96.33 28	1.07 759
929	863 041	30.47 95	96.38 46	1.07 643
930	864 900	30.49 59	96.43 65	1.07 527
931	866 761	30.51 23	96.48 83	1.07 411
932	868 624	30.52 87	96.54 01	1.07 296
933	870 489	30.54 50	96.59 19	1.07 181
934	872 356	30.56 14	96.64 37	1.07 066
935	874 225	30.57 78	96.69 54	1.06 952
936	676 096	30.59 41	96.74 71	1.06 838
937	877 969	30.61 05	96.79 88	1.06 724
938	879 844	30.62 68	96.85 04	1.06 610
939	881 721	30.64 31	96.90 20	1.06 496
940	883 600	30.65 94	96.95 36	1.06 383
941	885 481	30.67 57	97.00 52	1.06 270
942	887 364	30.69 20	97.05 67	1.06 157
943	889 249	30.70 83	97.10 82	1.06 045
944	891 136	30.72 46	97.15 97	1.05 932
945	893 025	30.74 09	97.21 11	1.05 820
946	894 916	30.75 71	97.26 25	1.05 708
947	896 809	30.77 34	97.31 39	1.05 597
948	898 704	30.78 96	97.36 53	1.05 485
949	900 601	30.80 58	97.41 66	1.05 374
950	902 500	30.82 21	97.46 79	1.05 263
N	N²	√N	√10N	1000 /N

N	N²	√N	√10N	1000 /N
950	902 500	30.82 21	97.46 79	1.05 263
951	904 401	30.83 83	97.51 92	1.05 152
952	906 304	30.85 45	97.57 05	1.05 042
953	908 209	30.87 07	97.62 17	1.04 932
954	910 116	30.88 69	97.67 29	1.04 822
955	912 025	30.90 31	97.72 41	1.04 712
956	913 936	30.91 92	97.77 53	1.04 603
957	915 849	30.93 54	97.82 64	1.04 493
958	917 764	30.95 16	97.87 75	1.04 384
959	919 681	30.96 77	97.92 85	1.04 275
960	921 600	30.98 39	97.97 96	1.04 167
961	923 521	31.00 00	98.03 06	1.04 058
962	925 444	31.01 61	98.08 16	1.03 950
963	927 369	31.03 22	98.13 26	1.03 842
964	929 296	31.04 83	98.18 35	1.03 734
965	931 225	31.06 44	98.23 44	1.03 627
966	933 156	31.08 05	98.28 53	1.03 520
967	935 089	31.09 66	98.33 62	1.03 413
968	937 024	31.11 27	98.38 70	1.03 306
969	938 961	31.12 88	98.43 78	1.03 199
970	940 900	31.14 48	98.48 86	1.03 093
971	942 841	31.16 09	98.53 93	1.02 987
972	944 784	31.17 69	98.59 01	1.02 881
973	946 729	31.19 29	98.64 08	1.02 775
974	948 676	31.20 90	98.69 14	1.02 669
975	950 625	31.22 50	98.74 21	1.02 564
976	952 576	31.24 10	98.79 27	1.02 459
977	954 529	31.25 70	98.84 33	1.02 354
978	956 484	31.27 30	98.89 39	1.02 249
979	958 441	31.28 90	98.94 44	1.02 145
980	960 400	31.30 50	98.99 49	1.02 041
981	962 361	31.32 09	99.04 54	1.01 937
982	964 324	31.33 69	99.09 59	1.01 833
983	966 289	31.35 28	99.14 64	1.01 729
984	968 256	31.36 88	99.19 68	1.01 626
985	970 225	31.38 47	99.24 72	1.01 523
986	972 196	31.40 06	99.29 75	1.01 420
987	974 169	31.41 66	99.34 79	1.01 317
988	976 144	31.43 25	99.39 82	1.01 215
989	978 121	31.44 84	99.44 85	1.01 112
990	980 100	31.46 43	99.49 87	1.01 010
991	982 081	31.48 02	99.54 90	1.00 908
992	984 064	31.49 60	99.59 92	1.00 806
993	986 049	31.51 19	99.64 94	1.00 705
994	988 036	31.52 78	99.69 95	1.00 604
995	990 025	31.54 36	99.74 97	1.00 503
996	992 016	31.55 95	99.79 98	1.00 402
997	994 009	31.57 53	99.84 99	1.00 301
998	996 004	31.59 11	99.89 99	1.00 200
999	998 001	31.60 70	99.95 00	1.00 100
1000	1000 000	31.62 28	100.00 00	1.00 000
N	N²	√N	√10N	1000 /N

Epilogue

Charles A. Bicking

STATISTICS IN MODERN
MANAGEMENT – TODAY
AND TOMORROW

The higher one looks in administrative levels of business, the more likely one is to find that decisions are based on data that are analyzed statistically and presented in tabular or graphic form. Chart meetings are part of the daily routine in many companies, and top administrators often provide leadership in the use of statistical methods.

For example, the president of a large company recently remarked that manufacturing management has three responsibilities: to produce at minimum cost, to maintain satisfactory quality, and to deliver when required. Yet, even though these objectives may often be in conflict timely and complete information was provided only on costs. The president encouraged management and supervision to state what data on quality and delivery they needed in their work, and then saw to it that this information was provided by the accounting staff. Thus, the idea of making better use of statistics radiates to all levels of modern administration, management, and supervision.

High-speed computers facilitate the use of statistics. There is danger, however, that in its enthusiasm the data-processing staff of a firm will merely "computerize" outdated clerical procedures instead of improving the quality of the information produced.

Suppose, for example, that you were concerned with the reporting of daily dollar values of order receipts. Following classical clerical procedures, you might also provide such information as "orders to date" for the current month, the same month last year, and last month of this year. You could express these data as cumulative totals or else take a small step towards efficient use of statistics by giving daily cumulative averages. So far, however, you would have simply picked up what any good bookkeeper might have accomplished manually. There are a number of shortcomings in the report, which will be considered next.

When the general manager reads your report for the first day of the month, suppose his eye falls on "orders received today." Unless your business is so unusual that daily order rates remain practically constant, he has received very little information from this figure. Usually, there will be some fluctuation in the arrival of orders. Unfortunately, however, there is a tendency to be optimistic when orders rise and to be pessimistic when they drop, even though they still fall within the limits of normally expected fluctuations. Without statistical analysis, of course, the limits are fuzzy or unknown, thus increasing the likelihood of unwarranted optimism or pessimism from day to day.

If you have reported daily averages to date this month, to date last month, and to date the same month last year, it was presumably to give the manager some idea of the direction of the trend of orders. On the first day of the month, however, each figure has the same characteristic shortcoming as "orders received today." On the second day averaging begins to smooth out the results, until by the middle of the month the limits of variation of the reported figures are about one-fourth of the limits of the first day's report.[1] Thus, every day during the month the manager is looking at figures of different reliability and meaning. Gradually, as the month proceeds, the figures approach the month's average, last month's average, and the average for the same month last year. The monthly averages are likely to vary at least in part as a result of seasonal, cyclical, and trend factors. The month's end summary will certainly have some value for the manager, but he would obtain far more guidance if the reports measured the

---

[1] Question to student: Why is there only a fourfold instead of a fifteenfold improvement by the middle of the month?

seasonal, cyclical, and trend values and provided information on the limits he should expect for variation.

A first step towards an improved report would probably be to show 30- or 31-day averages daily in place of the misleading variable averages discussed above. The information can be summarized over longer periods, and seasonal fluctuations, trends, and cycles can be identified. When this is done, the manager will be able to compare current performance in relation to past performance and expected performance. The expected values, based on seasonal variation, trend, and cycle, together with their confidence limits, could be extended into the future. Having planned a computing program with such statistical considerations in mind, an infinitely more useful report than otherwise possible could be prepared on the computer at no additional cost.

As has been emphasized by Dr. W. Edwards Deming, we must solve statistical problems with statistical knowledge, not substantive knowledge. Management desires to improve both the statistical and substantive aspects of the information on which it must operate. The era of computers opens new horizons for improved quality of information. The important function of statistics in modern management tomorrow will be in influencing computer programming so that statistical knowledge is applied to solve statistical problems.